Raspberry Pi Explained
for Radio Amateurs

by

Mike Richards, G4WNC

Published by
Radio Society of Great Britain of 3 Abbey Court, Priory Business Park, Bedford
MK44 3WH, United Kingdom
www.rsgb.org

First Printed 2020

Reprinted 2020 & 2021 (twice)

ISBN: 9781 9101 9384 6

Cover design: Kevin Williams, M6CYB
Editing: Ed Durrant, DD5LP
Production: Mark Allgar, M1MPA
Typography and design: Mark Pressland

The opinions expressed in this book are those of the author and are not necessarily those of the Radio Society of Great Britain. Whilst the information presented is believed to be correct, the publishers and their agents cannot accept responsibility for consequences arising from any inaccuracies or omissions.

Printed in Great Britain by 4Edge Ltd. of Hockley, Essex

Any amendments or updates to this book can be found at:
www.rsgb.org/booksextra

Contents

Contents (continued)

About the Author

Mike Richards, G4WNC

Inspired by his father, Jack, Mike took to radio and electronics construction at a very early age and they spent most of his teens building radios together. He was fortunate to have two excellent component stores locally and most Sunday evenings were spent window shopping. This informal apprenticeship served him well and set him up for a great career with BT that spanned 42 years. During that time, Mike worked on a diverse range of activities from planting poles to broadcast services. With BT, he was involved in the rapid development of data services and spent a significant period on the installation of digital telephone exchanges.

Mike first became licensed as G8HHA and was initially disillusioned with amateur radio as everybody was using commercial equipment. However, his interest was revitalised in the late 1970's when the Compukit UK101 personal computer was released. This gave the opportunity to experiment with computing and radio and he soon had the UK101 working with a friend's TRS80 over a 2m/70cms full duplex link. Soon after that he achieved his full amateur radio licence and became G4WNC. Mike has maintained a strong interest in the digital side of amateur radio ever since.

In parallel with his BT career, Mike started a writing career about 25 years ago when he was asked to take over the *Practical Wireless* magazine's RTTY column from Ron Ham. Since then Mike has been writing regular columns and reviews for a variety of magazines including the Radio Society of Great Britain's (RSGB) journal *RadCom*. Mike has also contributed to and written a number of RSGB books including *Virtual Radar Explained* which was published in 2010.

Dedication

The writing of this book has been something of a marathon and, as such, has required plenty of support to help me finally reach the finish line. There are a few people I need to thank that played a significant part in getting this book across the line. First, I would like to thank the RSGB for agreeing to publish the book and especially Mark Allgar, M1MPA, for his patience as he watched deadlines fly past with no output from me! I'm also grateful to Mark Pressland for his skills in transforming my words into such a fine layout. Editing a technical book such as this is not an easy task and I would like to thank Ed Durrant, DD5LP for his editing skills and encouragement.

Finally, but certainly not least, I would like to thank my family and friends for their tolerance and support during this project. Specifically, Trevor Pogson for listening to my complaints for the past couple of years.

This book is dedicated to my children Ruth, Rachel, Paul and my wife Elaine, G4LFM. Without their love and support this book wouldn't have happened.

Mike Richards, G4WNC
January 2020

Introduction

There are already plenty of Raspberry Pi books that cover the Pi from many angles, and I have bought many of them myself. However, I've yet to find one that feels like that vital reference you grab when you start a project. If you're anything like me, you are probably thinking 'what can I get the Pi to do right now'! So, I have started with a series of projects so that you can quickly make your Pi do something useful. This is followed by how to install popular radio applications and using the Pi for Software Defined Radio (SDR). After a while you'll want to create your own projects and that's where the other chapters will help you.

At this point, I also ought to come clean and make you aware that I am not a formally trained programmer. Whilst I have trained as a communications engineer, most of my computing and much of my electronics skills have been self-taught, driven by a desire to build a variety of projects. These ranged from communications receivers in my youth through to PA systems and music electronics as I joined the obligatory 60s band. That was followed by a wide range of amateur radio related projects along with an assortment of photographic applications. I was fortunate in living through the birth of the home computer and being able to learn using the likes of the Ohio Superboard, BBC-B Micro and the Amiga computers. One of the most frustrating aspects of this type of project-driven learning is the speed with which you forget the, rapidly assimilated, knowledge. My personal solution to that problem has been to keep a blog, where I record the important or hard-found learning points, so I can quickly familiarise myself when I return to a similar project at some later date (see www. g4wnc.com). This has proved very successful for me and saves a lot of time and effort. I therefore decided that a similar approach might work well for this book. My aim for this book is for it to become a go-to publication you reach for when you start a Raspberry Pi based project. You won't find any elegant programming solutions or cutting-edge code, but I hope you will find simple techniques and ideas that will help you to get things done with a Pi. I have included short code examples to help you understand how to get your project started.

Like it or loath it, the Raspberry Pi generally works at its best when running the Raspbian distribution of the Linux operating system. This distribution is continually evolving and provides easy access to a wide range of programming languages. An additional, and important, benefit comes from the huge selection of code libraries and hardware support that is built into the distribution. The net result is that Raspbian is far and away the most popular operating system for the Pi which in turn, makes it the best supported. It is therefore worth spending some time to get to know this operating system. To help you with this, I've included a chapter entitled Linux Essentials that attempts to capture the salient features and commands in an easy to digest format. Even if you don't remember the commands or how to use them, you can always refer back to this chapter for the answer. Similarly, the Pi Essentials chapter consolidates lots of tips and information about the Pi hardware that I hope you will find helpful.

Whilst every effort has been made to test the code samples and scripts used in this book, computing is a fast-evolving field and changes outside my control may compromise the included code. To help overcome this, I have setup a github repository that holds downloadable scripts (to save you some typing) along with any code corrections that may be necessary. You can find the repository at: https://github.com/g4wnc

The Pi Models

One of the great benefits of the Raspberry Pi platform has been the continuous development of the product. The Pi Foundation has always worked hard to keep in contact with their customers and this continuous feedback has helped shape the product development. The Pi Foundation have been very discrete when developing their new versions and have the knack of surprising the market with impressive features at a remarkable price point. Perhaps the biggest surprise in recent years was the launch of the Pi Zero at just £4! That model was so cheap, they gave one away free with each copy of one edition of the Magpi magazine.

Whilst all this development has been very welcome, the range of models can be a bit daunting to anyone new to the Pi. Whilst the main model B has become increasingly powerful, there are many applications that don't require the features or processing power of the latest model and can work very happily on an older model. In this section, I'll run through the various Pi models, to help you understand their differing capabilities.

Current models

Let's begin with the look at the current Pi range. The flagship model is the Pi-4B, **Figure 2-1**, and this is the model to chose if you're buying for the first time and want to start experimenting with the Pi platform. The Pi-4B uses a quad-core, 1.5GHz 64-bit Cortex-A72 processor combined with Gigabit Ethernet, dual-band Wi-Fi, Bluetooth, two USB 2 ports, two USB 3 ports and a choice of 1GB, 2GB or 4GB of RAM. The Pi-4B also includes dual micro-HDMI ports and can support two 4k displays. This combination makes the Pi-4B a seriously versatile computer for a wide range of applications and a serious rival to budget laptops. One important point while running the Pi-4 is heat management. The additional processing power of the Pi-4 increases the heat output and that needs to be managed to avoid the processor throttling-back due to overheating. When using the Pi-4 uncased on the bench you shouldn't need any additional cooling because the new metal packaging of the SoC (System on a Chip) keeps the temperatures at safe levels. However, as soon as you enclose the Pi in a case or add a HAT [1], you will need to increase the cooling capabilities. There are passive heatsinks available, but they are of limited value as they rely on a good airflow for their cooling. By far the best solution is forced air cooling and the 3rd party suppliers will no doubt develop all manner of ingenious devices. One of the early solutions, that I've found very helpful, is the Pimoroni Fan SHIM, **Figure 2-2**. This comprises a compact 30mm fan that's mounted on a tiny PCB and is a friction fit over the GPIO (general purpose input output) pins. In my tests, the Fan SHIM has dropped the Pi-4 processor's highest temperature by 30°C! In addition to providing excellent cooling, the Fan-Shim leaves all the GPIO pins available for reuse.

For those applications that don't need the power of the 4B, the previous flagship Pi-3B+, **Figure 2-3** is worth considering as the price is likely to drop. For applications that don't require Ethernet and multiple USB ports, the Pi-3A+, **Figure 2-4**, makes a very attractive proposition as it has the same processor and wireless capabilities as the Pi-3B+ but in a

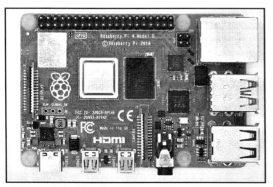

Figure 2-1: Pi-4B.

Figure 2-2: Pi-4B fitted with a Fan SHIM.

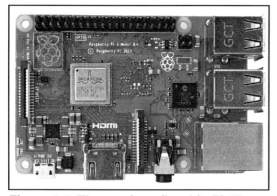

Figure 2-3: The previous flagship Pi-3B+.

Figure 2-4: Pi-3A+.

smaller package that costs around two-thirds of the price of the Pi-3B+.

For even smaller projects, that don't need multiple USB ports and a wired Ethernet, the Pi-Zero range has a lot going for it. The standard Pi-Zero is unbeatable at its super-low price (about £4 at the time of writing). However, if you need access to Wi-Fi or Bluetooth, the Pi-Zero-W, **Figure 2-5**, is often a better answer. In

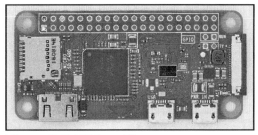

Figure 2-5: Pi Zero-W

addition to their very low cost and small size, the Pi-Zero models also boast lower power consumption, making them more suitable for battery powered applications.

Model comparison

I've split my comparisons into separate tables showing connectivity, processing power and power consumption to make the information more easily readable.

Pi connectivity

Table 2-1 shows the connectivity comparison between all the Pi models, except for the Compute module. I've deliberately omitted that module because it's primarily intended for industrial use by Original Equipment Manufacturers (OEMs)

Table 2-1: Raspberry Pi connectivity chart.

Pi Model	GPIO Pins	Ethernet	Wi-Fi	Bluetooth	USB2	USB3	Serial Camera	Serial Display
Pi-A	26	N	N	N	1	N	Y	Y
Pi-B	26	Y	N	N	2	N	Y	Y
Pi-A+	40	N	N	N	4	N	Y	Y
Pi-B+	40	Y	N	N	4	N	Y	Y
Pi-2B	40	Y	N	N	4	N	Y	Y
Pi-3B	40	Y	802.11n	4.1, LE	4	N	Y	Y
Pi-3B+	40	Y [1]	2.4+5GHz 802.11 b/g/n/ac	4.2, BLE	4	N	Y	Y
Pi-3A+	40	N	2.4+5GHz 802.11 b/g/n/ac	4.2, BLE	1	N	Y	Y
Pi-4B	40	Gigabit	2.4+5GHz 802.11 b/g/n/ac	5.0, BLE	2	2	Y	Y
Pi-Zero	40	N	N	N	1	N	Y [2]	N
Pi-Zero-W	40	N	802.11n	4.1	1	N	Y [2]	N

Note 1: The Pi-3B+ provides fast Ethernet using the USB controller and is faster than previous models but doesn't provide true Gigabit speeds.
Note 2: The serial camera port is only fitted to later Pi-Zeros and uses a narrower gauge socket.

Table 2-2: Pi processing power comparison chart.

Pi Model	SoC Device	Processor	Cores	CPU Clock	Video	RAM	SD/MMC
Pi-A	BCM2835	ARM 1176JZF-S	1	700MHz	1 x HD HDMI	256MB	SD
Pi-B	BCM2835	ARM 1176JZF-S	1	700MHz	1 x HD HDMI	512MB	SD
Pi-A+	BCM2835	ARM 1176JZF-S	1	700MHz	1 x HD HDMI	512MB	microSD
Pi-B+ .	BCM2835	ARM 1176JZF-S	1	700MHz	1 x HD HDMI	512MB	microSD
Pi-2B	BCM2836	Cortex-A7	4	900MHz	1 x HD HDMI	1GB	microSD
Pi-3B	BCM2837	Cortex A53 64-bit	4	1.2GHz	1 x HD HDMI	1GB DDR2	microSD
Pi-3B+	BCM2837B0	Cortex A53 64-bit	4	1.4GHz	1 x HD HDMI	1GB DDR2	microSD
Pi-3A+	BCM2837B0	Cortex A53 64-bit	4	1.4GHz	1 x HD HDMI	512MB DDR2	microSD
Pi-4B	BCM2711B0	Cortex A72 64-bit	4	1.5GHz	2 x 4k HDMI	1, 2 or 4GB	microSD
Pi-Zero	BCM2835	ARM 1176JZF-S	1	1GHz	1 x HD mini-HDMI	512MB	microSD
Pi-Zero-W	BCM2835	ARM 1176JZF-S	1	1GHz	1 x HD Mini-HDMI	512MB	microSD

and is not cost-effective for small projects. Although we are currently on version 4 of the Pi, the original generation boards did not have a numerical marking, so if your board just says Pi Model A or B, you can safely assume its version 1. If you need details of serial port access to the Pi, please refer to the separate section. As the Pi serial ports have undergone several changes I have provided a more detailed explanation in that section.

Raspberry Pi processor table

This section looks at the differing processing capabilities of the Pi models. Like many modern Single Board Computers (SBC), most of the hard work is done using a SoC (System on a Chip) integrated circuit. In these ICs the processor, graphics processor and other key components are combined into a single chip. As these components are usually hard-wired together, combining them in one chip reduces the circuit board complexity and keeps the overall cost down.

You will see from **Table 2-2**, that the Pi's processor has gone through several iterations. However, the graphics processor element has remained stable with a VideoCore IV providing full HD quality graphics support for all models except the

Pi-4. This current model uses the VideoCore VI processor for dual 4k resolution video outputs. The Pi-3 was the first to use the Cortex A53 64-bit processor, whilst the Pi-3B+ and A+ use a slightly different version of the processor that has a metal enclosure. This improves the heat dissipation and allows the default clock speed to be increased to 1.4GHz, without any additional cooling. The Pi-4 processor looks identical to the Pi-3 but is in fact a completely new and much more powerful device.

Raspberry Pi power consumption table

The power consumption will vary for different applications, so in **Table 2-3**, I've attempted to capture the consumption in a few common scenarios. The results are based on measuring the total consumption of real Raspberry Pi units where the current measured was the total drawn from the USB port connected power supply.

Under the hood changes

In addition to the headline changes between the Pi models, there have been a few technical changes that are worth noting. The first relates to the audio output. The Pi has always relied on HDMI for its main audio, but also has a simple Digital to Analogue Converter (DAC) that uses a Pulse Width Modulation (PWM) line from the processor, combined with a low-pass filter to provide an audio output. In the early boards, this suffered significant degradation due to power supply noise. However, from the introduction of the Pi-3, the audio has been improved with the addition of a new buffer chip between the processor and the low-pass

Table 2-3: Pi power consumption.

Pi Model	Board only *Note 1*	HDMI and Ethernet	HDMI and Wi-Fi	USB Max current draw
Pi-A	200mA	n/a	n/a	500mA
Pi-B	500mA	n/a	n/a	500mA
Pi-A+	180mA	n/a	n/a	500mA
Pi-B+	330mA	n/a	n/a	600mA/1.2A
Pi-2B	180mA*	290mA*	n/a	600mA/1.2A
Pi -B	260mA*	380mA*	360mA*	1.2A
Pi-3B+	390mA*	490mA*	520mA*	1.2A
Pi 3 Model A+	190mA*	n/a	290mA	*Note 2*
Pi-4B	560mA*	680mA*	710mA*	1.2A
Pi-Zero	150mA*	n/a	n/a	*Note 2*
Pi-Zero-W	160mA*	n/a	180mA*	*Note 2*

Note 1: Figures with * are measured, the rest are from the Raspberry Pi Foundation website [2].
Note 2: The maximum for these models is only limited by the external PSU and the micro USB connector.

filter. This has helped to clean-up the audio signal, whilst also increasing the available output power. In the early models, the audio output had its own 3.5mm jack, but the original jack has now been replaced with a new multi-pole 3.5mm jack that carries both the audio and the composite video output. See the Interfacing section for wiring details.

On-board power regulation has also changed significantly. Whilst the USB power socket still accepts a standard 5V input, most of the Pi components operate at 3.3V and below, so additional regulation has always been necessary. In the early boards, regulators inside the Broadcom SoC were used to supply the processor and GPU, whilst a linear 3.3V regulator did the rest. However, with the introduction of the Pi-2, external regulator chips were introduced for all supplies and the Pi changed to more efficient switch-mode regulators. This change also increased the amount of current that could be drawn from the Pi USB ports. The latest Pi models use a dedicated, 5 output, switch-mode regulator chip (MxL7704) to provide all the on-board supply needs for the Pi. The high efficiency of this regulator has helped to further reduce the overall Pi power consumption.

References
[1] https://www.raspberrypi.org/blog/introducing-raspberry-pi-hats/
[2] https://www.raspberrypi.org

Pi Projects

Introduction

In this chapter I'll present a selection of ready-to-go projects so you can achieve something with your Pi before you begin the deeper learning experience. When you announce to your friends that you've bought a Raspberry Pi. The first question you normally get is 'What is it?' quickly followed by 'What does it do?' Like most computers, the limits of what can be done are largely determined by your imagination. Whilst the projects in this chapter will help you get the Pi to do something useful, the real fun comes when you start thinking of your own applications. That's where the rest of this book comes to your assistance. The more technical chapters of this book are packed with lots of practical solutions, code snippets and general tips to point you in the right direction to success-fully complete your projects.

Pi basics

I'll begin by running through a few essentials that you need to get the most out of these projects. Each of these items are covered in more detail elsewhere in the book but the simpli-fied instructions here are designed for those new to the Pi.

In **Figures 3-1 to 3-5**

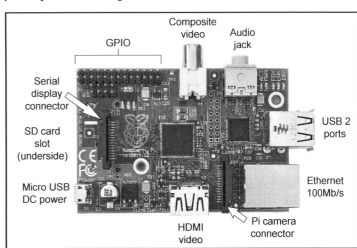

Figure 3-1: Pi-B connections.

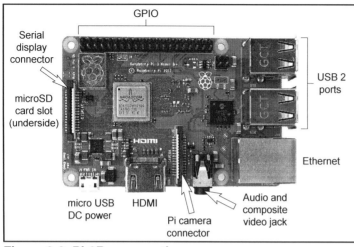

GPIO

Serial display connector

microSD card slot (underside)

USB 2 ports

Ethernet

micro USB DC power

HDMI

Pi camera connector

Audio and composite video jack

Figure 3-2: Pi-3B+ connections.

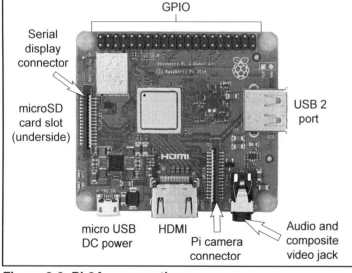

GPIO

Serial display connector

microSD card slot (underside)

USB 2 port

micro USB DC power

HDMI

Pi camera connector

Audio and composite video jack

Figure 3-3: Pi-3A+ connections.

I've shown the connection details for all the Pi board layouts. You will also need an SD or microSD card and I suggest you use a 16GB class 10 card. One of the big differences between the Pi and many other computers is the use of a memory card as the main storage for the operating system and programs. The card does the same job as the hard drive in many other computers. Whilst there are a few drawbacks with SD cards, they do make it very easy to completely change the function of the Pi with a simple card swap. This is a big plus, given its intended use as an educational machine. If you get into trouble, you can just plug-in a new operating system card and start again. SD cards with a variety of programs pre-installed can be purchased from several sites eg. Amazon, PiHut, Pimoroni, www.g4wnc.com.

Installing an Operating System:

I suggest you stick with the official Raspbian version of Linux as it has been optimised for use with the Pi and is regularly updated. If you're completely new, you may have bought the NOOBs software on a microSD card, in which case you don't need to worry about burning SD cards for now.

For those that don't have a preconfigured or NOOBS microSD card, here are the steps to create your own SD card with the Raspbian operating system installed. I'm assuming most will be using a Windows computer, but Apple and Linux computers will follow the same steps.

Before you start, you will need the following:

1. Internet connected computer.
2. A USB microSD card reader.
3. A blank 8GB or 16GB microSD card, preferably Class 10 but most will work ok.

If you're unsure what microSD card to buy, I have been using Kingston Canvas 16GB class 10 cards for some time now without any problems. Transferring the Raspberry Pi operating system to the card requires software that is designed to create a bootable system disk, you can't simply copy the image. There are several systems available, but Balena-Etcher is one of easiest to use and includes automatic validation of the new microSD card so you can be certain that the card

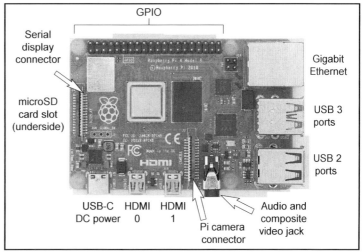

Figure 3-4: Pi-4B connections.

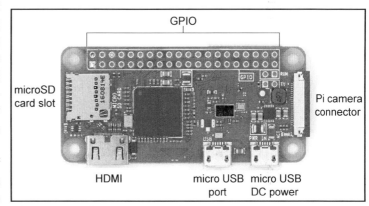

Figure 3-5: Pi Zero connections.

is properly created. In addition to writing "flashing" a single memory card, Balena-Etcher can simultaneously burn several microSD cards on the same computer.

Here are the steps to download and install the Balena-Etcher program:

1. Run a web search for 'Balena-Etcher' and navigate to the Balena-Etcher website (https://www.balena.io/etcher/)
2. The website normally identifies your computer's operating system automatically so you can click the download button to transfer the latest Balena-Etcher installer to your computer.
3. Run the downloaded installer program to complete the installation of Balena-etcher.

With Balena-Etcher installed, the next step is to download the latest Rasp-

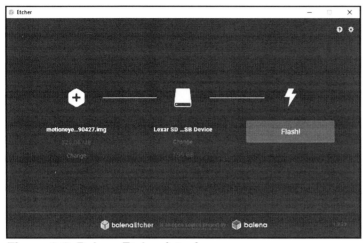

Figure 3-6: Balena-Etcher interface.

bian image from the Raspberry Pi website. Here's the steps to use:

1. Navigate to the Pi site at raspberrypi.org/downloads/.
2. Click the Raspbian icon and select Raspbian Buster with desktop and recommended software. (Buster is the latest Raspbian version at the time of writing).
3. Select Download Zip. NB: If you're familiar with torrents you can save download bandwidth by following the torrent link.

4. When the download completes you can progress on to flashing the microSD card with the image.

Flashing SD cards with Balena-Etcher: When you start the software, you will see that there are just three steps to burning an image, **Figure 3-6**:

1. Select the image file that you want to burn. That's the file that you downloaded.
2. Select the SD cards you want to burn to. NB: Be careful here because external USB hard drives connected to your PC may also be listed and you want to avoid overwriting those.
3. Click the Flash button and the process will start.

Balena-Etcher will copy the image to the SD card and then verify the card against the image to ensure it is error free. If there is a problem, you will see a failure message.

The first time that you start your Pi from this new SD card you will be taken through the setup process to configure such things as language to be used, the keyboard and your network connection. The setup process also includes an update from the internet of the image. You should allow plenty of time for this step.

The Raspbian distribution

The Raspbian Linux operating systems is packed with useful software to enable you to do a myriad of tasks without having to load additional software. In its default state, the desktop is very clean with a Task bar running along the top of the screen and a single wastebasket icon on the desktop.

Understanding the taskbar

The top left of the Task bar begins with the Pi menu button and this provides easy access to all the software that's currently installed. Next to that is the web browser, which is the Chromium open source browser. You are free to add other browsers but at the time of writing, Chromium was regarded as the best performer. The next application on the task bar is the File Manager that provides simple navigation of the Pi file system. The final application is the Terminal emulator that's used to enter command line statements. As you become more familiar with Linux you will appreciate the power of the command line.

To the top right of the task bar are a selection of status icons. These provide both information and controls and you will find that left and right clicks on them perform different actions. Starting from the left we have the Bluetooth icon that you can use to turn Bluetooth on or off and to start pairing actions with other devices. Next comes the Network icon that shows a pair of arrows if you're using cabled Ethernet or three quadrants if you have a Wi-Fi network connection. Hovering over the Network icon will show the connection status and IP address of the available connections. (Most of the projects in this book require your Pi to be connected to the Internet over your LAN or WLAN (WiFi) to enable software to be downloaded. The speaker icon gives access to sound controls and a left-click will open the volume control, whereas a right-click lets you select the audio device when more than one is available. Finally, we have the system clock that reports the system time.

In addition to these fixed items, any running programs will temporarily appear in the task bar and their icons can be used to quickly access applications that have been minimised or to switch between applications.

The Pi menu and installed software

The Pi menu is the main route to the installed software and you will use this a lot. As new users will be unfamiliar with many of the applications, I'll give a brief synopsis here.

Programming menu

BlueJ Java IDE: This is a dedicated IDE (Integrated Development Environment) for writing Java code.

Geany Programmer's Editor: This is a general-purpose IDE that can be used to program in a variety of languages. It includes syntax checking for the more popular languages and can be used to validate and test software.

Greenfoot Java IDE: An open source IDE for teaching Java code developed by Kings College London.

Matematica: This may not be installed by default in every distribution but Wolfram Mathematica is a modern technical computing system spanning most areas of technical computing — including neural networks, machine learning, image processing, geometry, data science, visualizations, and others.

Mu: A very simple to use Python IDE that includes debugging tools.

Node-RED: This may not be installed by default in every distribution but is a very powerful visual programming tool that's ideal for handling messages from hardware sensors, controllers and other IoT (Internet of Things) devices.

Scratch and Scratch 2: Scratch is a visual programming language that's been developed to help teach good programming principles to younger students.

Sense HAT Emulator: The sense HAT is an add-on board for the Pi that was originally designed to support Tim Peake's work whilst on the International Space Station. The board includes sensors for temperature, pressure, humidity, and orientation. This software emulates a sense HAT and can be used to help develop and test software written for the Sense HAT.

Sonic Pi: This is an easy-to-use electronic music creation package. It has built-in tutorials and plenty of sound samples to help you get started.

Thonny Python IDE: This is the Python IDE recommended by the Pi team. It includes full syntax highlighting and checking and includes run and debugging facilities.

Wolfram: This may not be installed by default in every distribution but Wolfram Alpha is a computational knowledge engine or answer engine developed by Wolfram Alpha LLC, a subsidiary of Wolfram Research.

Education menu

SmartSim: This is a very simple yet powerful visual tool for designing and testing digital logic circuits.

Office menu

The Office menu contains the full LibreOffice set of applications that provide the standard applications for an office computer. LibreOffice can handle most of the Microsoft Office™ file formats and files are usually interchangeable. Here's a run through of the applications:

LibreOffice Base: This is a dedicated database application.

LibreOffice Calc: For creating and manipulating spreadsheets and is similar to Excel™.

LibreOffice Draw: This is a drawing package that can be used for a wide range of applications from flow charts to site drawings.

LibreOffice Impress: For creating slide presentations. Similar features to PowerPoint™.

LibreOffice Math: A specialist program for creating and editing complex mathematical formulae.

LibreOffice Writer: Similar to Word™, this application is used for creating text documents.

Internet menu

Chromium Web Browser: This open source browser has been optimised for the Pi and provides the best browsing experience.

Claws Mail: This is a standard mail program for those that have yet to change to webmail.

VNC Viewer: The Pi team have partnered with RealVNC to make their re-mote-control application available to Pi users. The VNC viewer can be used to access and control remote PCs using the Pi.

Sound & video menu

VLC Media Player: An open source, universal, media player that can be used to play all media files from audio through to 4k video.

Graphics menu

Image Viewer: A simple viewer that, unusually, has its controls located in the bottom status bar.

Games menu

Minecraft: This is an adapted version of the popular Minecraft game.

Python Games: A collection of simple Python games.

Accessories menu

Archiver: A tool to create or expand compressed files that supports all the common Linux compression systems.

Calculator: A useful desktop calculator that can handle a wide range of cal-culations.

File Manager: Provides a Windows explorer like application for navigating the Pi file system.

PDF Viewer: For viewing PDF files.

SD *Card Copier:* A very useful tool that you should use regularly to back-up your microSD card.

Task Manager: Provides a tabular view of all the running applications along with memory and CPU usage.

Terminal: Provides a terminal session for communicating with Linux via the command line.

Text Editor: A simple text editor called Leafpad.

Help menu

Provides access to several useful guides and support services.

Preferences menu

Add/Remove *Software:* This is a useful graphical tool that helps you find and install or remove software for the Pi. The software available through this tool has been approved for use with the Pi.

Appearance Settings: This panel lets you change the look of the desktop.

Audio *Device Settings:* Settings for internal and external audio devices.

Keyboard and Mouse: Configure keyboard mouse and other input devices.

Main Menu Editor: Add or remove applications from the main menu.

Raspberry Pi Configuration: Configure the Raspberry Pi system.

Recommended Software: Install additional programs which are recommended for use on the Pi.

Run option: This provides a quick way to run an application providing you know its name.

Shutdown option: Provides options to either shutdown, reboot or logout of your Pi.

Project 1 - Raspberry Pi security/wildlife camera

Here's a very useful project to build a motion detecting camera system that was originally designed as a security camera but also does a great job of spotting wildlife movements in your garden. In this project, the Pi acts as the hub of the security network where it can use the official Pi Camera Module or many 3rd Party Internet and web cameras. The underlying software is a Linux Open source package appropriately called Motion. This software manages the live streams from cameras and triggers recordings when motion events are detected. Motion software can be installed on most Linux systems and is packed with sophisticated features. The sophistication itself causes a problem because, with so many choices, it's easy for the new user to get lost. It's also very easy to misconfigure Motion and that leads to more frustration when it seemingly refuses to do what you ask! To overcome the complexity issues, several programmers have built friendly front-ends to Motion. In my view the best of these is MotionEyeOS, **Figure 3-7**. The author has combined the sophistication and performance of Motion with a much simpler, browser based,

front-end and a custom Linux operating system (based on BuildRoot).
The net result is a surprisingly small
yet powerful application for any
situation where you want to detect
and record motion. MotionEyeOS
is supplied as a free, downloadable
SD card image and is regularly updated. In addition to working on all
Pi models, MotionEyeOS also runs
on several of the Pi's competitors.

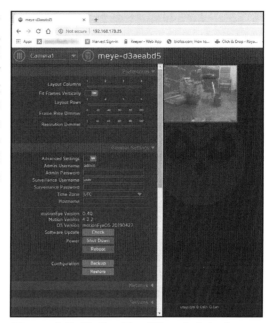

What do you need?
1. Raspberry Pi - any model
2. 4GB or greater SD or
   microSD card, to suit your
   Pi model
3. Pi 5V power supply
4. Raspberry Pi camera or a
   USB webcam.

Figure 3-7: MotionEyeOS web interface.

   NB: If using a Pi Zero you need an adapter cable because the Pi-
   Zero uses a finer pitched camera connector.
5. Keyboard, mouse and monitor. NB: This is only required for initial
   configuration.
6. Network connection for the Pi. I strongly recommend using an Ethernet connection for the initial configuration, especially if you're new
   to the Pi. Once everything is working with the Ethernet, it's easy to
   change over to Wi-Fi later.

The first task is to download the MotionEyeOS SD image and flash it to your
microSD card. The best method is to use another, Internet connected, Windows,
Mac or Linux computer, that has Balena-Etcher installed, as described in the
Installing an Operating System section.

Here are the steps:
1. Begin by visiting the MotionEyeOS home page here:
   https://github.com/ccrisan/motioneyos/wiki
2. On this site, navigate to the Getting Started section and click the
   'supported devices' link. Scroll down the list of boards until you
   find your Pi model and click on the link next to 'latest version'. After
   selecting where to store the img.xz file, this will start the download.
   As MotionEyeOS is built on a minimal Linux system, the download is
   quite small at around 50MB.

3. Once the download completes, follow my earlier instructions to Install an Operating System to your blank microSD card.

With your flashed SD card, you can return to your Pi and begin the installation and configuration by following these steps:

1. Insert the microSD into the Pi with the contacts nearest the PCB.
2. If you're using a Pi camera, gently lift the black plastic retaining bar at the top of the Pi camera connector, **Figure 3-8**.
3. Insert the Pi camera cable with the bare contacts nearest the HDMI socket, **Figure 3-9**.
4. Once the cable is seated you should only be able to see the top edge of the contacts, **Figure 3-10**.
5. Gently push the cable retaining bar back in place to secure the camera cable.
6. Connect the HDMI monitor and the USB mouse/keyboard.
7. Finally, connect the power lead and apply power.

Figure 3-8: Pi camera connector.

You should see signs of life with the green LED flickering on the Pi along with four raspberries appearing on the screen. You will also see screen messages reporting creation of the disk partitions and the system will reboot. When it's ready, you will be presented with a line of text that looks similar to, **Figure 3-11**, with the last line something like: meyec42e35d4 login:

Figure 3-9: Pi camera cable and connector.

Although the software invites you to login, there's no need, because MotionEyeOS is designed to be managed through a web interface. Let's begin the setup:

On the Pi monitor you will see a line that looks like this:

Interface eth0 has IP address 192.168.178.44/24

This is the IP address of your Pi on the local network and you need to make a note of this. In this example the IP address is: 192.168.178.44.

Figure 3-10: Pi camera cable fully inserted.

On any other computer that's connected to your local network, open a browser and enter the address you noted into the address bar of a browser, omitting the final three characters, ie, /24. If you have a Pi camera connected, this should return a screen similar to **Figure 3-12** with a live-view image displayed. Don't worry about the orientation of the camera at this stage as we can easily fix that later. Now that the system is showing signs of life, we need to complete some basic configuration. Here are the steps:

Figure 3-11: MotionEyeOS screen after power-up.

1. In the Web browser view of MotionEyeOS, click on the head and shoulders icon at the top left of the screen to display the Login prompt.
2. Enter admin at the Username but leave the Password blank and click Login.
3. You will now be returned to the main screen.
4. Click the round button with three horizontal lines (top left) to open the settings menu.
5. Scroll to the General Settings section and turn-on Advanced Settings.

Figure 3-12: MotionEyeOS live view.

6. The default video frame rate is set to 2 frames per second, but we need to change a few of the trigger settings to improve motion capture.
7. Scroll down to the Motion Detection section and set the following:
    a. Captured Before = 3 - This tells the software how many frames to store from before movement was first detected. You can adjust this later to suit the situation.
    b. Captured After = 3 - This tells the software how long to keep recording after the trigger movement has stopped.
    c. Minimum motion frames = 3 - This sets the minimum number of continuous motion frames that need be detected before a recording will start. The default setting of 20 frames is too long for

many situations, so activity could be missed. If you find 3 frames too sensitive, you can increase this setting later.

8. Having completed the changes, the next vital step is to click the Apply button at the top of the screen. Without this action the changes will be lost!

9. Return to the top left of the screen and click on the circle with three vertical lines to close the settings.

That completes the basic configuration and you can start testing it to make sure it captures activity in the way you want.

Adding Cameras:

If you are using a webcam or a network camera, you may find that it is not automatically detected by MotionEyeOS. This is quite common and easily fixed as follows:

1. Access MotionEyeOS via a browser and click on the head and shoulders icon to login.

2. If there are no cameras detected, you will see a line of text at the top of the screen inviting you to add a camera. Click on this. If you already have at least one camera detected and you want to add more, click on the drop-down box in the top left of the screen and choose: add camera…

3. You will see the Add Camera… panel where you can choose the camera type and camera. For a webcam this will normally be 'Local V4L2 Camera' or 'UVC Camera'. If you're using a network camera, you need to enter its IP address or URL and a name.

4. The motion trigger events that we set earlier are specific to each camera, so you need to repeat those settings for each new camera.

Changing File Storage:

In its default configuration, MotionEyeOS stores all the captured videos to the Pi microSD card. This can quickly fill the card, so most users choose a different storage option. The simplest is to add a USB memory stick or an external USB hard drive to the Pi. To set this up, follow these steps:

1. Login to motionEyeOS using a web browser.

2. Open the settings (circle with three horizontal bars)

3. Scroll down to the File Storage section.

4. Choose your storage device from the drop-down menu, **Figure 3-13**. USB devices will usually show-up with the name of the device followed by the location in brackets, ie, Samsung Portable (/dev/sdb1)

5. When you've completed the selection, click the Apply button to save the changes.

If you want to store the files on a centralised server, choose the Network Share option in the File Storage section and you must enter the IP address and shared name of the server. Once this has been entered, click the Test Share button to make sure it's working OK and don't forget to press Apply to commit the changes.

Using Wi-Fi:

The simplest way to configure Motion-EyeOS to use Wi-Fi is to start with an Ethernet connection and use the web browser to access the settings and enable Wi-Fi. Follow these steps:

Figure 3-13: MotionEyeOS storage settings.

1. Login to motionEyeOS using a web browser.
2. Scroll down to the Network section of the settings.
3. Turn Wireless Network on and enter the SSID name and wireless key for your Wi-Fi network. Leave IP Configuration on Automatic (DHCP).
4. Click Apply to commit the changes. This will automatically reboot the Pi and change to the Wi-Fi connection.

Summary

In this short tutorial we've only scratched the surface of what MotionEyeOS can achieve and you should refer to the MotionEyeOS Wiki for more detailed instructions (https://github.com/ccrisan/motioneyeOS/wiki). With its ability to operate with multiple cameras, a Raspberry Pi-3 running MotionEyeOS could be configured as the hub for a full home security camera system. This could use Pi Camera Modules mounted on a Pi-Zero-W to create a network of low-cost network connected surveillance cameras. The Pi-Zero-W is particularly attractive in this role because the official Pi-Zero case includes a lid with a camera mounting clip. As you can see from **Figure 3-14**, this makes a very neat combination that just requires a 5V power source.

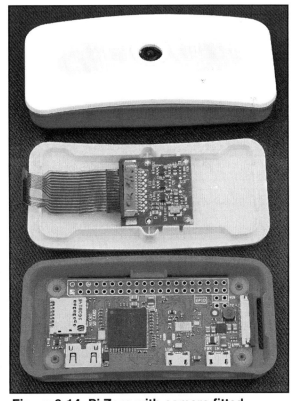

Figure 3-14: Pi Zero with camera fitted.

Project 2 - WSPR beacon

Weak Signal Propagation Reporter (WSPR) is a low speed radio data transmission mode developed by Joe Taylor, K1JT to probe radio propagation paths. WSPR signals use a very slow data rate and only require a few Hz of bandwidth. The result is a signal that can be detected under extremely poor propagation conditions. WSPR transmissions carry only basic information, which is normally the originating station's callsign, their Maidenhead location and their transmit power. The data rate is extremely slow with each message taking 2 minutes to transmit. Stations providing WSPR beacon facilities usually comprise a computer running the WSPR software connected to the main amateur radio transceiver and antenna system. Whilst this works very well, it does tie-up the main station. The Raspberry Pi offers an alternative solution thanks to some innovative work by enthusiasts. Pin 4 of the GPIO on the Pi is connected to a Pulse Width Modulation (PWM) line on the Pi processor. This has many conventional uses but several users realised that this line could be used to generate radio frequency signals. Initial work focussed on using Frequency Modulation (FM) of the PWM line to transmit music on the VHF/FM band (illegally). However, it was soon noticed that this feature could be used to generate RF signals on the amateur bands and a WSPR beacon was proposed. As WSPR is such a slow-speed data mode, directly generating the RF signal is well within the capabilities of the Pi.

Figure 3-15: WSPR filter board fitted to a Pi Zero.

What do you need?

1. Raspberry Pi, with an Internet connection (Wi-Fi or LAN)
2. Monitor, Keyboard and mouse (only required for setup)
3. Pi power supply
4. WSPR antenna filter

Filtering and protection:

There are two main problems with using the Pi GPIO pin to generate radio signals. The first is the high harmonic content due to the square waves used on the PWM line. This waveform contains very strong odd-order harmonics and cannot be used without some filtering. The second problem is the risk of damage to the Pi Processor because the GPIO pin is connected directly to the processor chip. As a result, any static build-up on the antenna could easily destroy the Pi processor. Both problems are easily solved by using an external filter board. Whilst there are several good designs on the Web, I opted for a ready-built unit from the Tucson Amateur Packet Radio (TAPR) group. Their filter board uses the design by Zoltan Doczi, HA7DCD and mounts directly on the Pi GPIO pins, **Figure 3-15**

and **Figure 3-16**. Rather than just providing a simple low-pass filter, Zoltan uses a bandpass filter that's been optimised to reduce carrier noise. He has also included a single FET amplifier stage to isolate the antenna from the GPIO pins and added a transient protection diode to discharge any static build-up. The net result is a very compact filter board, with a useful +20dBm (100mW) output that's ready to be directly connected to the antenna.

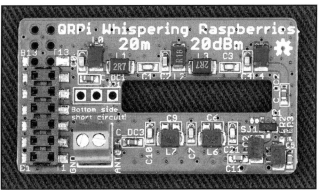

Figure 3-16: The WsprryPi filter board.

WSPR Software:

To bring this project to life we need the software to control the PWM pin and generate the WSPR signal. One important point to note here is that the software must be operated with the Pi connected to the Internet. This is necessary because WSPR requires accurate timing to work correctly and the software uses Internet based timeservers to keep the Pi clock accurate. The internet time is also used to calculate the Pi reference clock error to ensure the transmit frequency is correct.

The Wsprry software we need is available for free download from the Github site, and here are the instructions to download, compile and install the software:

1. Open a terminal session (Ctl-Alt-T)
2. Enter: git clone https://github.com/g4wnc/WsprryPi.git
3. Change to the new directory by entering: cd WsprryPi
4. Enter the following to build the software: make
5. Enter the following to complete the installation: sudo make install

That completes the software installation and you should connect your filter to the Pi and a dummy load to the antenna terminal.

Testing and Operation:

The software has a built-in test-tone facility that is very helpful when checking the basic function of the board. Here are the steps to generate a test-tone:

1. Open a terminal session (Ctl-Alt-T)
2. Enter: sudo ./wspr --test-tone 14.097e6
3. To stop the transmission enter: Ctrl-C

This will begin transmission of a single frequency of 14.097MHz. You can now use an oscilloscope, RF voltmeter or another receiver to check the signal quality. If all is well, you can start a WSPR transmission with the following:

```
sudo ./wspr --repeat --offset --self-calibration G4WNC
IO90 20 20m
```

In this example, you need to replace G4WNC with your callsign and IO90 with the first four characters of your Maidenhead locator. The penultimate entry (20) is the output power in dBm whilst the final item (20m) is where you specify the band to be used.

When you're happy that the transmitter is working OK, you can connect the antenna and start transmitting. You will find more detailed instructions for using the software on the Github site at: https://github.com/g4wnc/WsprryPi

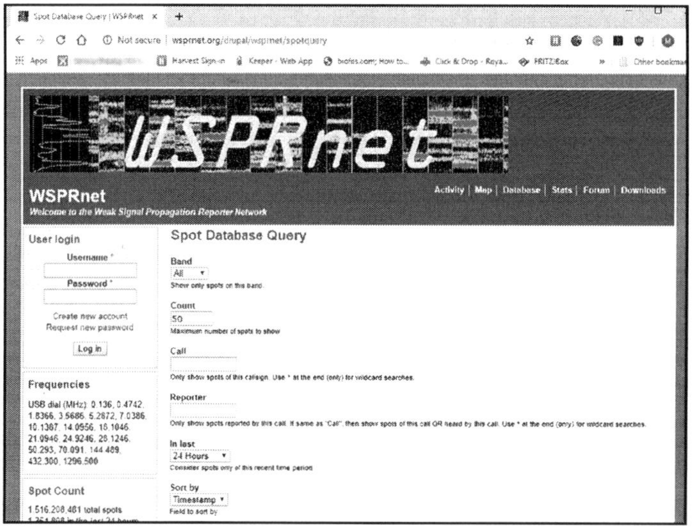

Figure 3-17: WSPRnet database search page.

When your Pi-transmitter has been running for a while, you should head over to the WSPR website (wsprnet.org) to see if anyone has heard you. When you reach the site, select the Database tab. This will take you to a screen where you can query the database to see if your transmission has been heard, **Figure 3-17**. Here's a guide to setting up the query:

1. Select the band you're using
2. In the Call box enter your callsign
3. Leave the other settings at the default and click the Update button.

This will return a list of all the stations that have heard your call along with useful information such as the signal to noise ratio (SNR) of your signal and distance to the receiving station.

Summary

The WsprryPi software we've used for this project makes very light demands on the Pi and so is a good way of utilising one of the less powerful or older Pi models, such as original Pi-B or a Pi-Zero-W. You can also continue to use the Pi to run other software whilst running WsprryPi.

Project 3 - SDR receiver server

This project utilises a USB radio and TV receiver dongle that has become popular for watching terrestrial digital TV and listening to DAB radio broadcasts on a PC, **Figure 3-18**. Most of these dongles use the Realtek RTL2832 chip to digitise the radio signal from the on-board tuner. Soon after they were released, an un-documented feature of these chips was discovered that enabled the In-phase and Quadrature (IQ) signals to be made available via the USB port.

Those of you familiar with modern digital radio techniques will recognise that the IQ signals are at the heart of all modern Software Defined Radios (SDR) as they facilitate the demodulation of just about any signal. The dongles supporting this feature are now commonly known as RTL-SDR dongles. In this project we use a Raspberry Pi with an RTL-SDR dongle to make the IQ data available on the local network so it can be accessed from anywhere on your local network. This can be used in many ways. One common use is to position the Pi and RTL-SDR dongle in the radio shack, connected to the main antenna system. You could use the server via your local network listen to the RTL-SDR dongle from the comfort of your living room or maybe out in the garden.

Another common use is to improve VHF or UHF operation. For the best VHF and UHF reception, it's important to mount the antenna in the clear and as high as possible. This normally results in a long feeder cable between the antenna and the receiver, which introduces losses and adds noise. The con-ventional solution is to use expensive, low-loss, antenna feeder cable or mount a masthead preamp at the antenna. An alternative solution is to mount the Pi, complete with an RTL-SDR dongle, close to the antenna. This allows for a very short antenna feeder, whilst the link back to the radio shack is made using cheap CAT-5 Ethernet cable. The overall result is better VHF/UHF reception combined with the convenience of being able to operate anywhere that's within reach of your local network.

What do you need?
1. Any Pi model with an Ether-net port.
2. microSD card loaded with the latest Raspbian Linux.
3. RTL-SDR dongle.

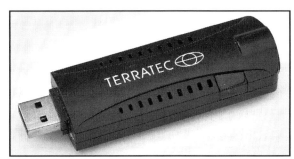

Figure 3-18: Popular TV dongle.

4. Keyboard, mouse and monitor (Only required for setup).
5. Pi power supply
6. A Windows PC with SDR Sharp software installed

Installing the software:

The installation process is straightforward, and you can use the Pi Add/Remove software tool as follows:

1. From the Pi menu button choose Preferences - Add/Remove Software.
2. In the search box enter: rtl-sdr and press enter
3. Following a short wait whilst it searches for possible software, a list of possible programs will be returned.
4. Enter rtl-sdr in the search box and press enter You will probably find the latest version of the package s highlighted as in, **Figure 3-19**
5. Make sure the option: Software defined radio receiver for Realtek RTL2832U (tools) is highlighted.
6. Click the tick-box on the left to select the software for installation
7. Click Apply or OK at the bottom-right to install the software.
8. The installer will ask for your Raspberry Pi system password and then retrieve and install the selected package along with any other packages that may be required.
9. When it's finished if you pressed "Apply" you can close the Add/Remove software panel. If you pressed "OK" it will close itself.

Reboot the Pi and when it's up and running, you need to test the software

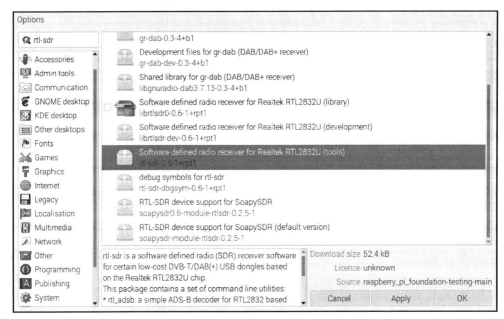

Figure 3-19: The RTL-SDR software highlighted.

and the RTL-SDR dongle to make sure they can talk to each other. Here is the step-by-step process:

1. Plug-in your RTL-SDR Dongle
2. Open a terminal session (Ctl-Alt-T)
3. Enter the following: rtl_test -t
4. Leave this to run for a couple of minutes, until it completes.

You should see a screen that shows that it has found your dongle and then lists its capabilities. Because rtl_test can work with multiple dongle tuners, you may see a 'no tuner found' message. That's OK providing it did find one tuner. If your dongle is not recognised, try rebooting the Pi and running the test again. If it's still not recognised, you may have an incompatible dongle.

Once you have a successful test result you can move on to check the operation of the server. The server is started with a single command, as shown below:

1. rtl_tcp -a followed by the IP address of your Pi.
2. To find the IP address of your Pi enter: hostname -I

For example

if your Pi has the IP address 192.168.1.44, the command to start the server becomes:

```
rtl_tcp -a 192.168.1.44
```

When the server starts you will see a message to report that the dongle has been found and is listening.

Once the server has started, you need to check that the whole system is working by following these steps:

1. Go to a Windows PC on your local network and start SDR Sharp.
2. From the Sources drop-down menu choose RTL-SDR (TCP), **Figure 3-20**.
3. Click the cog icon and enter your Pi IP address in the Host field, then close that panel by clicking on the X.
4. Make sure you

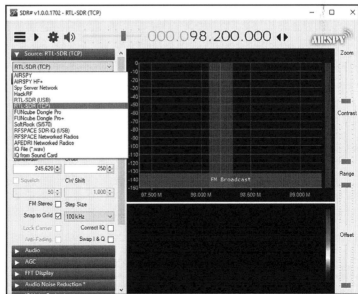

Figure 3-20: Selecting the RTL-SDR dongle in SDR Sharp.

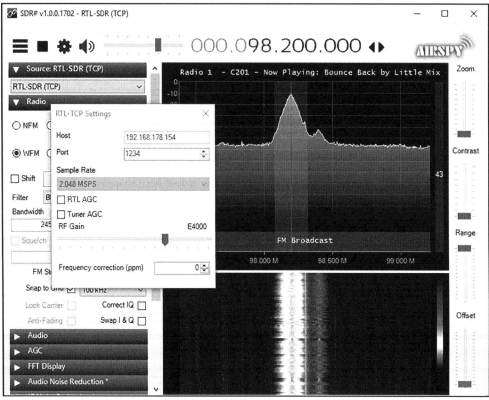

Figure 3-21: Configuring the dongle in SDR Sharp.

have attached an antenna to the dongle and click the Play icon (>) at the top of the screen to start receiving.

5. Tune SDR Sharp to a known active stations frequency. The VHF/FM band is a good place to begin.

6. Click the cog icon again and click the Tuner AGC box or set the RF Gain to about three-quarters, **Figure 3-21**.

If all is well, you should be able to receive plenty of stations.

Project improvements:

So far in this project we have installed the server software from source and configured it to work with SDR Sharp. Now that we've completed the setup, we don't really need the monitor, keyboard and mouse. However, we do still need to be able to start the server. There are two ways to do this. The first is to run the Pi in what's known as headless mode. This is where we access the Pi over the network from another computer. That way we can remotely open a terminal session and enter the command to start the server. For details of how to do this, look at the headless section in the Pi Linux chapter. The more elegant solution would be to start the server automatically when the Pi is powered-up. This is relatively easy to do and is also covered in the Pi Linux chapter.

Project 4 - Workshop heater controller

The first three projects have used software that others have created, but for this project, we'll be writing our own Python program. At the end of the project you will have a useful Pi thermostat that can easily be upgraded to add more sensors, heaters, air conditioning units, etc.

What do you need?

1. Pi - any model.
2. Monitor, keyboard and mouse (only for configuration).
3. A microSD card loaded with Raspbian Linux.
4. Pi power supply.
5. Energenie UK Pi-Mote board.
6. Temperature sensor type DS18B20 with a 4.7k resistor and hook-up wires
7. Soldering iron

Introduction:

Whilst the Pi makes a great low-cost desktop computer, the provision of the GPIO expansion pins makes it an ideal candidate from what is often called 'real world' projects. This means linking the Pi to household appliances and other devices to create all manner of interesting applications. In this project, you will learn how to use the Pi to measure temperatures and to switch mains-powered appliances.

Using a Pi to control mains appliances could be fraught with danger due to the lethal voltages involved. However, the spread of wireless controlled mains sockets provides a very neat solution. Energenie UK (//energenie4u.co.uk/) are one of the major players in the world of wireless controlled mains sockets and produces the PiMote interface board that's specifically designed for the Pi, **Figure 3-22**. This board, when used with the Energenie Python library, mimics an Energenie remote controller so the Pi can remotely switch mains sockets. The switchable sockets are all rated for the full 240V 13 amps, so can safely be used to control any plug-in appliance including heaters.

For the temperature measurement, I'm using the Dallas Semiconductor DS18B20 sensor. This is a sophisticated temperature sensor housed in a small 3-pin plastic case similar to that used for transistors. The sensor has just three connections and requires a single resistor to complete the circuit, as shown

Figure 3-22: Energenie Pi-Mote mains socket controller.

in **Figure 3-23**. This sensor uses the 1-wire transmission protocol to supply its temperature readings to the Pi. Despite its diminutive size, the sensor has its own processor and can be interrogated to reveal its temperature. If you want to add more sensors they can simply be connected in parallel. This is possible because each sensor has a unique ID, and so can be individually addressed.

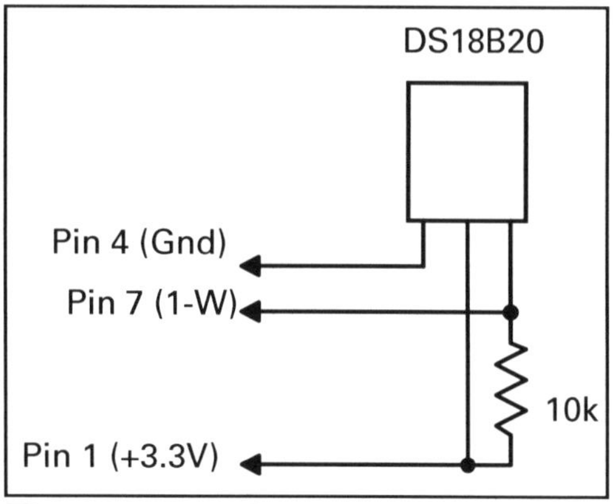

Figure 3-23: DS18B20 thermal sensor wiring.

Program Outline:

Let's start with an outline of what I've designed the program to do. The main task is to keep the workshop heated to 18°C during the day and 8°C at night. However, I want to have easy access to the software so I can change the day or night temperatures. I also might want to change the times of the changeover between day and night. To handle these changes, I've created a set of variables near the top of the program, so they're easy to find and amend.

Structuring the program:

As with all the examples in this book, I'm using Python 3 and making use of pre-written code libraries for many of the more complex tasks. The GPIOzero library has the code to communicate with the Energenie Pi Mote board and is providing the TimeOfDay module. This module gives us a quick way to check if the current time is between the start and stop times set in TimeOfDay. In this case it is used to control the switching between day and night heating settings. I'm using 'time' from the 'datetime' module so that we can use sensible formatting to enter the start and stop times. There's also a 'sleep' function from the 'time' module that's used to add a delay into the program loop. Finally, I'm using the w1thermsensor module to read the temperature from the

Figure 3-24: Python heater program.

DS18B20 sensor. With all those modules doing the hard parts, we only need write the code to join them all together to create the controller.

In **Figure 3-24**, I've shown the complete Python program and I suggest you type-up your program using either the Geany or Thonny program editor from the Programming menu. If you'd rather just download these files, I have stored copies on github and you can use the following actions to download them:

1. Open a terminal session (Ctl-Alt-T)
2. Enter: git clone https://github.com/g4wnc/PiHeater.git
3. This will download all the files into the PiHeater directory.

Here's a more detailed description of how the program works:
Line 1 contains what's known as a shebang and tells Linux where to find the Python 3 interpreter.

Lines 2 to 5 are the commands to import the code modules we'll be using.

Lines 7 to 12 are used to setup the main parameters of the program. Sensor1 identifies the temperature sensor that we want to use. The daytime variable holds the start and finish times that we want to be treated as the daytime period. The following two lines are used to specify the desired temperature for the day and night periods. The final line in this section tells the Energenie module that we're expecting the heater to be plugged into socket group 1.
With the setup complete, we now move on to define a couple of custom functions. The first of these is called h_timer and can be seen in lines 14 to 19. its only purpose is to set the appropriate target temperature for the time of day and return that value for use elsewhere in the program.

The second function (lines 21 to 26), takes the target temperature from h_timer, reads the temperature sensor (line 22) and turns the heater on or off as appropriate. To prevent the heater from repeatedly turning on and off, I've added some hysteresis by setting the heater to turn off when the temperature is 1°C above the target but only turn back on when it is 1°C below the target. As a result, the workshop temperature will slowly cycle between those two trigger points.

With all the work happening in the imported modules and the two custom functions, the main program loop is reduced to just three lines, with one line handling all the work! Line 28 starts a loop that will continue for ever, whilst Line 29 starts the thermostat function and includes a call to the h_timer to get the target temperature. Line 30 just adds a 1 second delay to slow the loop. In a practical installation you would use a 5-minute (300 second) or greater delay so the temperature is checked every 5 minutes.

Preparation:
Before you can run this program, you need to do some preparation as follows:

1. Open a terminal session and enter: sudo apt -y install python3-w1thermsensor (enter) this will take a few seconds to complete.

2. Click the Pi menu and select Preferences - Raspberry Pi Configuration - Interfaces tab.
3. Scroll down to 1-Wire and click the enabled button.
4. Power-down the Pi.

The next step is to mount the Pi-Mote controller on the Pi and connect the wires for the temperature sensor. The Pi-Mote is a simple push fit onto the GPIO pins and you should use the manufacturer's guidance for this. Wiring-up the temperature sensor requires some soldering and there are two ways to make the connection to the Pi. The first is to solder it directly to the Pi-Mote board or you can solder it to the GPIO pins on the bottom of the Pi. In both cases you need to be careful to connect-up correctly. I've shown the connections in **Figure 3-25**.

Figure 3-25: Pi-Mote mounted on a Pi-1.

Once the Pi-Mote and temperature sensor are connected, you can power-up the Pi. The next task is to link the Pi-Mote with the Energenie socket that you're using for the heater. This is a simple process that begins by generating a control signal from the Pi. The simplest way to do this is with a short Python 3 program as follows:

1. From the Pi menu choose Programming - Thonny Python IDE
2. This will open the IDE so you can start typing in the following program:

```python3
#!/usr/bin/python3
from gpiozero import Energenie
from time import sleep
heater = Energenie(1)
while True:
    heater.on()
    sleep(2)
    heater.off()
    sleep(4)
```

3. When you've entered the code, click the Save icon and save it as:

```
test.py
```

4. You can now click the Run icon to start the program.

If there are any typos, you will see an error message in the Shell panel at the bottom of Thonny. The error message should identify the line where the problem has been detected.

With the Python program running press and hold the green button on the remote socket until the LED flashes. This indicates that it's entered its learning mode. You should find that the socket quickly recognises the Pi control signal and will start toggling on and off every 4 seconds. The Energenie sockets use a non-volatile memory so they will remember that they're linked to the Pi, even when removed from a mains power socket.

Before we can move on to test the operation of the main heater program, you need to find the hardware ID of your DS18B20 temperature sensor and paste it into line 8 of the heater program. The simplest way to do this is have Thonny and a terminal session open on the screen. To find the sensor ID enter the following in the terminal session:

```
w1thermsensor ls
```

This will list all the devices connected to the 1-wire bus that, in our case, will just be the DS18B20 sensor. You should get a response similar to the following:

```
1. HWID: 000004d3f8b3 Type: DS18B20
```

Use the mouse cursor to copy the HWID, ie 000004d3f8b3 in this example. Move to the Python program and paste from the clipboard to replace the existing sensor ID at the end of line 8. Save the program and you're done.

Testing:

The easiest way to test the program is to amend the timing and temperature settings at the start of the program. For example, you could alter the start or finish time to be just a couple of minutes ahead of the time now. You could then set the temperature close to the current ambient temperature. That way you could heat the sensor with your fingers and cool it by blowing on it. You should then be able to see the heater plug turning on and off in response. Another useful debugging tip is to insert a print statement to display the temperature detected by the sensor. Here's a line you can add as line 32:

```
print(sensor1.get_temperature())
```

This will print out the sensor temperature in the Shell panel at the bottom of the Thonny IDE. This debugging technique is very common and you can add print statements at various stages of the program to track variables and help identify bugs. The format for the print statement is as follows:

```
print(name_of_variable)
```

Sometimes you will want to add some text to the print statement so you know which variable is being reported. Here's an example:

```
print("variable a = ", name_of_variable)
```

Project summary:

The heater timer is a useful project for the home or workshop and this basic Python script can be adapted and improved in many ways.

4 marker top right

Installing Popular Radio Applications

Introduction

With the arrival of the Pi-2 and latterly the Pi-3 and 4, the Pi now has enough processing power to handle the decoding of all the popular radio data modes. This has been helped by the availability of some very good software packages for the Linux operating system. The following software packages are by far the most popular, so I will run through their installation in detail:

FLDIGI by David Freese, W1HKJ

WSJT-X by Joe Taylor, K1JT

JS8Call by Jordan Sherer, KN4CRD

QSSTV by Johan Maes, ON4QZ

Direwolf by John Langer, WB2OSZ

YAAC by Andrew Pavlin, KA2DDO

Xastir by Xastir development team.

All of these programs are all well supported with plenty of online forums and documentation to guide you through the operating procedures. As the guides are regularly updated, I won't attempt to repeat the operating information here.

Points to note

The instructions here assume you are starting with the latest release of Raspbian and that you only have one version of the target software in the Downloads folder. If you have more than one version the instructions will fail due to my use of the * wildcard to reduce the amount of typing and simplify the instructions. All the applications require an audio feed to and from your transceiver and the simplest way to provide that is with a simple USB soundcard. When selecting a soundcard, it's useful to get one with a short USB tail as this keeps the surrounding USB ports clear for use by other devices. You can also use dedicated data mode interfaces such as the popular Signalink range.

Linux install errors

Once you start regularly using the apt install command to add software, you will probably encounter errors at some point. Whilst the response on the command line might initially confuse you, Linux generally shows you where the problem rests and often provides the solution. In most cases the error will be related to a missing or outdated dependency.

When installing software, it is important to make sure you have the latest list of available software packages. This is important because the Install command uses the packages list to find all the software dependencies for the program being installed. If this is out-of-date, it may not be able to find the correct package, so the install will fail. Updating the packages list is simply a matter of running the update command as follows:

```
sudo apt update
```

I always recommend using a fresh download of Raspbian when beginning a new project. However, it's important to run the update and upgrade commands on this new image. This is necessary because of the way updates are managed. The Raspberry Pi Foundation provide updates on a continuous basis, but these updates are not immediately applied to the download image. By way of example, at the time of writing, the download image was nearly 3 months old. The only way to ensure you have an up-to-date image is to download and install the latest image then run the following command line:

```
sudo apt update && sudo apt upgrade && reboot
```

This will update the packages list, upgrade all the installed packages to the latest versions and reboot the Pi. It is good practice to do this prior to any new installation.

Common errors and solutions

Typos:
Mistyping is by far and away the most common cause of failed Linux commands. It's an unfortunate fact of life that we are very poor at spotting our own mistakes. A simple solution, that works for me, is to do something entirely different for a while. When I return to the problem the typo is usually obvious.

Fix-missing error:
Sometimes, 'apt install' will fail and suggest using '--fix-missing' command to resolve. There are a variety of causes, but it is safe to use the suggested

command as follows:

```
sudo apt install --fix-missing
```

If that doesn't solve the problem, you could also try:

```
sudo dpkg --configure -a
```

Lock file errors:

Occasionally, you may see a lock file error when you try to recover from a failed 'apt install'. Lock files are generated by Linux to prevent multiple processes from accessing and changing the same file. Once a process has completed, the lock file is automatically deleted. However, if a process fails, it may leave the lock file in place. This is easily solved by deleting the apt lock file with the following commands:

```
sudo rm /var/lib/apt/lists/lock
```

```
sudo rm /var/cache/apt/archives/lock
```

You should now be able to re-run the install.

Start afresh:

If you've encountered errors during installation and worked out the solution, it is often worth completely removing the offending software and starting again. The command to remove a program is:

```
sudo apt purge 'program name'
```

This will remove all the program and configuration files except those stored in the Pi directory. You can delete those files manually.

Google is your friend:

Linux is a very well supported operating system and you will find lots of help available via a Google search. If you encounter an error that you can't resolve, simply copy and paste the error, from the terminal into Google. You should get plenty of results. If you are signed-in to Google, you will also have access to their search tools. I use these tools to filter the results to the past year to ensure I see current solutions.

Installing FLDIGI

FLDIGI was the first data modes software that I managed to get working on a Pi and I used it extensively for PSK-31 work, **Figure 4-1** (overleaf). In this mode it will even work on a Pi-2. However, The Pi-3 and later versions are by far the best choice as they support all the included data modes. FLDIGI software is the most complex of the data mode applications to install because it needs to be built from source. Whilst you will find a copy of FLDIGI in the Raspbian repository, it is likely to be old. At the time of writing, the current FLDIGI version was 4.1.08 , whilst the repository was carrying version 4.1.01-1 . To check the repository

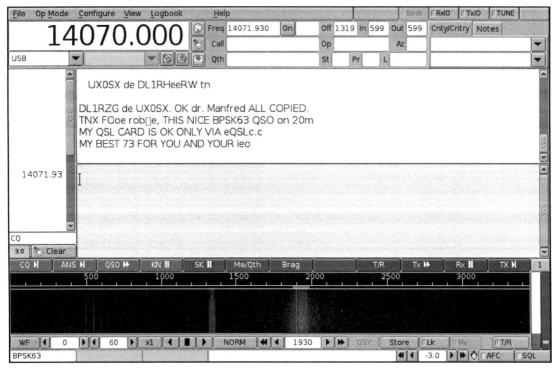

Figure 4-1: FLDIGI running PSK-31 on the Pi.

version, enter the following command in a terminal session:

```
apt-cache policy fldigi
```

There are a couple of options for installing FLDIGI and both require some preparatory work. The first is to begin with a fresh install of the Raspbian operating system. This also needs to be updated with all the latest fixes and releases. We can do that with the following command in a terminal session:

```
sudo apt update && sudo apt upgrade -y && reboot
```

The next step is to increase the swap space allocation for the Pi. The swap space is temporary storage space on the SD card. This is normally kept at a low value of 100MB to help extend the life of SD card. However, whilst installing FLDIGI, additional swap space is necessary.

Here's a step-by-step guide to expanding the swap space:

1. From a terminal session enter: sudo nano /etc/dphys-swapfile
2. This will open the configuration file for editing
3. Scroll down to the line: CONF_SWAPSIZE=100
4. Change this to read: CONF_SWAPSIZE=1024
5. Press Ctl-X followed by Enter to save and exit the editor
6. Reboot to Pi to activate the new swap space.

One simple solution for installing FLDIGI, is to use the excellent script produced by Edward Valasek, K3HTK. This is available for download from: http://indyham.com. The script is undergoing continual improvement and does all the hard work for you. I suggest you download the script and follow the installation instructions on the Indyham site. When you've completed the installation, repeat the swap space process from earlier, but revert to the original setting, i.e: CONF_SWAPSIZE=100

As the Indyham script may not be available in the future, I will also cover manual installation here. In addition to updating and increasing the swap space, we need to give othe Pi access to the appropriate source files. This is a simple task that requires a modification to the apt sources.list file. Here's the process:

1. Open a terminal session and enter: sudo nano /etc/apt/sources.list
2. Look for a line that starts: #deb-src
3. Delete the # from the beginning of the line.
4. Press Ctl X followed by Return to save and close the file.
5. Reboot the Pi.

To simplify the installation process, we need to install the aptitude package with the following command:

```
sudo apt install -y aptitude
```

Now we can update the packages list with:

```
sudo aptitude update
```

The next step is to install all the dependencies to support FLDIGI. We can do this like so:

```
sudo aptitude build-dep fldigi
```

This command will take a while to run and will present you with a few options along the way. Just answer Y to all of these. The libxft-dev package should have been installed during this process but, as it's sometimes missed, we can now add it manually along with the PulseAudio volume control:

```
sudo aptitude install libxft-dev pavucontrol
```

That completes all the preparatory work so we can now start installing FLDIGI. This is a lengthy process, especially the make command so be patient. The following steps have been written for FLDIGI 4.1.08. If installing a different version, you will need to change the version numbers.

Here is the install process:

Open a terminal session (Ctl-Alt-T) and enter the following commands:

```
cd ~

wget http://www.w1hkj.com/files/fldigi/fldigi-4.1.08.tar.gz

tar xvzf fldigi-4-1-08.tag.gz

cd fldigi-4.1.08
```

```
./configure

make

sudo make install
```

On completion you can enter fldigi on the command line to start FLDIGI. However, it's generally more convenient to add the program to the menu system. Here's how to do that:

1. From the Pi menu button choose Preferences then Main Menu Editor
2. Click on Applications then click New Menu - name this Radio Apps and press OK.
3. Click on Radio Apps in the left column and select New Item
4. Click the Command box and enter /usr/local/bin/fldigi
5. Now click the name box and enter: FLDIGI and click OK.

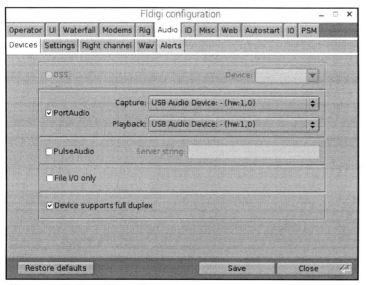

Figure 4-2: FLDIGI audio configuration.

You will now find a new group in the menu called Radio Apps with FLDIGI as its only program. Before moving-on, don't forget to repeat the swap space process from earlier, but revert to the original setting, i.e: CONF_ SWAPSIZE=100. You also need to reboot the Pi.

The first time FLDIGI runs you will be prompted to enter your station details, sound card selection, etc. You can skip this and access it later via Configure on the top bar of the FLDIGI screen. In addition to your station details you need to tell FLDIGI which sound card to use. To setup the sound, within FLDIGI open configuration and select the Audio tab. Tick the PortAudio box and select USB Audio Device for both the Capture and Playback devices, **Figure 4-2**. NB: You must have your USB sound card plugged-in before starting FLDIGI.

To adjust the audio levels, use the following:

1. From the Pi menu select Sound & Video – PulseAudio Volume Control.
2. This will open the volume panel.
3. Select Input Devices and make sure your USB audio card is selected in the drop-down.
4. At the bottom of the panel make sure All Except Monitors is selected.
5. Now adjust the Microphone slider to set the input level to FLDIGI.

6. Select the Output Devices tab and make sure your USB card is still selected.
7. At the bottom of the panel, make sure Show All Output Devices is selected.
8. You can now adjust the audio out from FLDIGI using the Speaker slider.

It's worth keeping the PulseAudio volume panel open when operating as it's a very convenient tool for trimming audio levels.

WSJT-X

Joe Taylor's WSJT-X comprises a superb suite of weak signal modes for everything from moon-bounce to HF DX work, **Figure 4-3**. The software enjoys continuous development and new features are added regularly. At the time of writing, FT8 is completely dominating HF data modes along with WSPR being used extensively to test antenna coverage and to check propagation conditions.

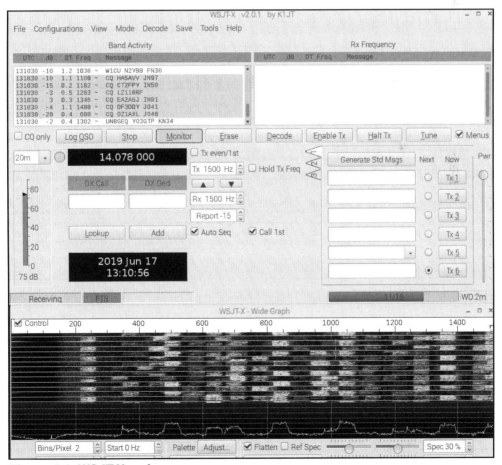

Figure 4-3: WSJT-X main screen.

Although originally focussed on Windows computers, the software has been made available for various Linux based systems including the Raspberry Pi. The software is distributed as packaged binary files for the Pi so is very easy to install. Here is a web link to the download files: https://phyics.princeto.edu/pulsar/k1jt/wsjtx.htm

To install WSJT-X from the download package follow these steps:

1. Open a terminal session.
2. Install the prerequisites by entering:
   sudo apt install libqt5multimedia5-plugins libqt5serialport5
   sudo apt install -y libqt5sql5-sqlite libfftw3-single3
3. Open a web browser and navigate to:
   https://physics.princeton.edu/pulsar/k1jt/wsjtx.html
4. Scroll to the bottom of the page and download the latest WSJT-X package for the Raspberry Pi. You need the download package that ends with: _armhf.deb You may be asked if you want to keep the file and you can answer yes.
5. Return to the terminal session and enter the following:

```
cd ~

sudo dpkg -i ~/Downloads/wsjtx_2.1.2_armhf.deb
```

6. NB: amend the file name in step 5 to match your download.

The first time you run WSJT-X you will be prompted to enter essential information about you and your station. This must be completed as transmissions from WSJT-X are blocked until the station and operator details have been provided. The WSJT-X suite of programs are very well supported and I recommend reading the excellent User Guide available here: https://physics.princeton.edu/pulsar/k1jt/wsjtx-doc/wsjtx-main-2.1.2.html. There is also a very active user forum on Groups.IO called WSJTX. Please remember that the WSJT-X data modes are designed for weak signal use and you should always use the minimum power level to sustain the contact. Using high power simply spoils the mode for others. If you want to update an existing WSJT-X installation, just run steps 3 to 6 and the new version will replace the existing one whilst retaining all your personal files and data.

JS8Call

JS8Call is a derivative of WSJT-X and has been created to provide a chat mode option for the popular FT8 data mode, **Figure 4-4**. Most of the code is that same as WSJT-X, but the protocol has been modified to allow free-text messages to span several transmission sequences. The home page for JS8Call can be found at: http:// js8call.com and includes download links, guides and a useful FAQ. To install JS8Call on the Pi, follow these steps:

1. Install the prerequisites using steps 1 and 2 of the WSJT-X install

procedure I described earlier.

2. Open the web browser and navigate to:

   `files.js8call.com/latest.html`

3. Select the Raspberry Pi download (this will end with armhf.deb)

4. Open a terminal session (Ctl-Alt-T) and enter the following commands:

   `cd ~`

   `sudo dpkg -i ~/Downloads/ js8call*`

5. That completes the installation.

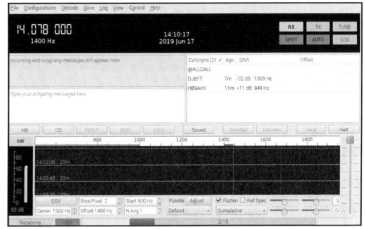

Figure 4-4: JS8Call main screen.

You can start JS8Call by double-clicking the desktop icon and then use the configuration wizard to enter your call and station details. For operational guidance, please refer to the JS8Call web page where you'll find up-to-date information. As with WSJT-X, upgrading to the latest version is very easy as you simply repeat steps 2 to 5 of the installation process.

Installing QSSTV

QSSTV written by Johan Maes, ON4QZ is the best Slow Scan TV application for Linux and works very well on the Pi-3, **Figure 4-5**. The download and operating instructions can be found on Johan's website at: http://users.telenet.be/on4qz/

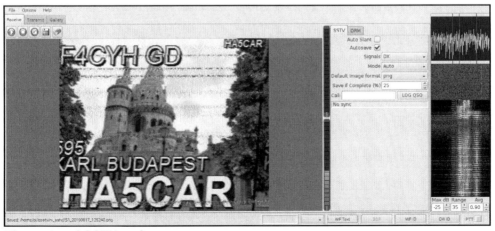

Figure 4-5: QSSTV main screen.

index.html .

Here is a step-by-step guide to installing QSSTV:

1. Open a terminal session (Ctl-Alt-T) and make sure you're in the Pi home directory:

```
cd ~
```

2. Install the prerequisites with the following lines:

```
sudo apt update

sudo apt install -y g++ libfftw3-dev qt5-default
libpulse-dev

sudo apt install -y libhamlib-dev libasound2-dev
libv4l-dev

sudo apt install -y libopenjp2-7 libopenjp2-7-dev
```

3. Open a browser and navigate to the QSSTV website: http://users.telenet.be/on4qz/

4. Follow the download link and download the latest version.

5. Enter the following lines in a terminal session to install the software:

```
cd ~

unzip ~/Downloads/qsstv*

cd ~/qsstv*

qmake

make (NB: this will take a long time so be patient)

sudo make install
```

6. That completes the installation

To run the program either use the menu entry (Usually found under Education) or open a terminal session and enter: qsstv. As with the other data mode software, it's important to complete the configuration when you first start the program. To configure QSSTV go to the menu bar and choose Options - Preferences. On the Operator tab you can enter your details. Once that's complete move to the Sound tab and select your USB soundcard. If you are using a common USB soundcard, you should click to activate ALSA and select hw:CARD=Device. DEV=0--USB Audio Device, USB Audio. You can also setup the CAT control via the

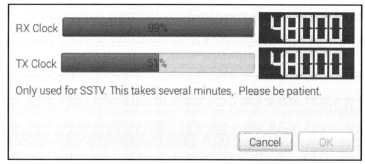

Figure 4-6: QSSTV sound card calibration panel.

CAT tab but QSSTV runs well with VOX transmit/receive switching and it doesn't have any frequency or mode setting options so there's not really a need for a CAT link. The final task before you can start operating is to calibrate your soundcard. Receiving good quality SSTV images demands an accurate reference clock and QSSTV relies on the sound card sampling clock for its timing. These clocks are not always accurate so QSSTV has a built-in clock calibration system to compensate for inaccurate clocks. To use the calibration your Pi must be connected to the Internet because it uses Internet time servers as the reference for the timing checks. When you're ready, you can start the calibration by selecting Options - Calibration. This will open the sound card calibration panel, **Figure 4-6**. The calibration will take a while and the final correction details will be automatically applied upon completion.

Dire Wolf

Amateur packet radio has traditionally required a dedicated hardware modem known as a Terminal Node Controller (TNC). This had two main functions, the first of which was to manage the AX-25 protocol used by Packet Radio to break messages into standard packets and reassemble them at the receiving end. The second function was to convert the packet data stream into audio tones that can be sent and received using a standard SSB or FM transceiver. As the computing power available to radio amateurs has increased, those functions can now be comfortably handled in software on the main PC so a TNC is no longer required. With the arrival of the Pi-3 the Pi now has enough processing power to support Packet Radio software. For those that would still prefer to use hardware, the TNC-Pi is a good choice as it fits neatly on top of the Pi and provides full TNC functionality. However in this tutorial, we're going to install the Dire Wolf software that, in combination with a USB soundcard, provides all we need for general packet radio operation. In addition to providing the basic Packet Radio management Dire Wolf can perform as an APRS tracker, Digipeater, IGate (Internet Gateway) and an APRS gateway. Dire Wolf can also be used with other software to run more advanced applications.

Before you Start: If you are intending to use APRS with downloaded maps you will need your system on a large microSD card because map data files tend to be very large. I recommend using a 32GB card.

Installing Dire Wolf: To ensure you are using the latest version, it is best to build Dire Wolf from the source code. Here's the step-by-step process:

Open a terminal session (Ctl-Alt-T) and enter the following commands:

```
cd ~

sudo apt install -y libasound2-dev libudev-dev

git clone https://www.github.com/wb2osz/direwolf

cd direwolf

make
```

```
sudo make install

make install-conf

make install-rpi
```

That completes the installation, so we can move on to the basic configuration. I recommend setting your station as an IGATE (Internet gateway) so you can contribute to the local APRS coverage. To do that, you will need a passcode that is calculated from your callsign. An Internet search will reveal plenty of online resources to do the conversion for you. A good example being the APRS Passcode Generator from Peter Goodall, 2M0SQL at: https://apps.magicbug.co.uk/passcode. As with most Linux configuration files, the # character is used to indicate that line is to be treated as a comment only. Most of the configuration simply requires deletion of the # to make the required lines active.

To complete Dire Wolf configuration use the following steps:
1. Open a terminal session (Ctl-Alt-T).
2. Enter the following to open the Dire Wolf configuration file:

    ```
    sudo nano ~/direwolf.conf
    ```

3. With the config file open, scroll down to the block titled 'FIRST AUDIO DEVICE PROPERTIES' and then scroll to the line that begins with #ADEVICE plughw:1,0.
4. Delete the # at the beginning of the line.
5. Scroll down to the section titled 'CHANNEL 0 PROPERTIES' and to the line containing 'MYCALL NOCALL'.
6. Replace NOCALL with your callsign. NB: This must be all capitals.
7. In the same section you should check the modem speed. The default setting is MODEM 1200, which is correct for standard VHF/UHF operation. However, you can select 300, 1200 or 9600 by removing the # from the appropriate line in this section.
8. Scroll down to the DIGIPEATER PROPERTIES section.
9. Delete the # from the line beginning #DIGIPEAT 0 0...
10. I recommend configuring Dire Wolf as an Igate server because your station then becomes a contributor to the wider APRS network and so increases its coverage. This is particularly important if you live in a remote area.
11. Scroll down to the Internet Gateway section and select the APRS server for your location. For Europe and Africa it will be: euro.aprs2.net, whilst in North America it would be noam.aprs2.net.
12. Scroll to the line with IGSERVER and remove the # from the front of the line and add the server name as in 11.
13. In the same section, remove the # from the front of the IGLOGIN and add your callsign (in capitals) and your passcode.
14. To save and close the file enter: Ctl-X followed by Y followed by Enter.

```
File  Edit  Tabs  Help
Reading config file direwolf.conf
Audio device for both receive and transmit: plughw:1,0  (channel 0)
Channel 0: 1200 baud, AFSK 1200 & 2200 Hz, E+, 44100 sample rate / 3.
Note: PTT not configured for channel 0. (Ignore this if using VOX.)
Ready to accept AGW client application 0 on port 8000 ...
Ready to accept KISS TCP client application 0 on port 8001 ...

Now connected to IGate server euro.aprs2.net (88.217.98.197)
Check server status here http://88.217.98.197:14501




M5PDL-9 audio level = 8(4/3)   [NONE]   _::|||_:

MIC-E, normal car (side view), Yaesu FTM-100D, En Route
N 50 44.9800, W 001 52.6300, 0 MPH, course 28, alt 89 ft

Digipeater MB7UW audio level = 8(4/3)   [NONE]   |||||||:_

Telemetry
Seq=872, A1=186, A2=255, A3=129, A4=62, A5=119, D1=1, D2=0, D3=0, D4=1, D5=0, D6
=1, D7=1, D8=1
```

Figure 4-7: Dire Wolf message screen.

That completes the basic set-up, so we can check that everything is working. In Europe the best frequency for packet activity is 144.8MHz whilst in North America it's 144.39MHz. In most densely populated areas, you should find plenty of short APRS transmissions on those frequencies.

With your rig and the Pi running and connected, either double-click the Dire Wolf icon on the desktop or open a terminal session and enter direwolf. If all is well, you will see a new terminal window, **Figure 4-7**, with messages confirming that the audio device has been found and that Dire Wolf is ready to accept AGW and KISS applications. If you don't see these messages, there's probably a mistake in the direwolf.config file so you need to double-check the file for typos.

Once Dire Wolf is running properly, you should see messages printed on the screen following receipt of a packet transmission. You will also see a line that shows the audio level. If this is red your audio is too high, so you need to reduce it. Go to Preferences - Audio Device Settings and select your USB Audio Device, select Capture and use the audio level control to adjust the level, **Figure 4-8**. If there are no controls displayed, click the Select

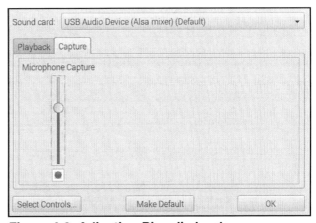

Figure 4-8: Adjusting Pi audio levels.

Controls box in the lower left of the panel and make sure the Speaker, Microphone and Microphone Capture boxes are all ticked.

That completes the basic configuration of the Dire Wolf software and it should be working as a standard Packet TNC with APRS IGATE and Digipeater services. I suggest you read the excellent User Guides that will have been installed on the Pi as part of the Dire Wolf build process. All the guides can be found in: /usr/local/share/doc/direwolf. If you're using Dire Wolf for general packet radio, rather than APRS, you might want to consider activating the beaconing. This will cause Dire Wolf to periodically transmit your station location and capabilities so others can find you. This can be activated via the beaconing section of the configuration file. Please make sure you don't beacon too frequently, every 30 minutes is plenty. If you are planning to use APRS, it's simpler to manage beacon transmission from the APRS software.

There are several dedicated APRS applications available but Xastir and YAAC work well on the Pi. Let's begin with YAAC.

YAAC Installation

YAAC (Yet Another APRS Client!) written by Andrew Pavlin, KA2DDO is a cross platform application written in Java and is completely self-contained, **Figure 4-9**. To run YAAC on the PI you just need to have the latest Java runtime for the Pi installed along with YAAC. Here's a guide to installing YAAC on the Pi:

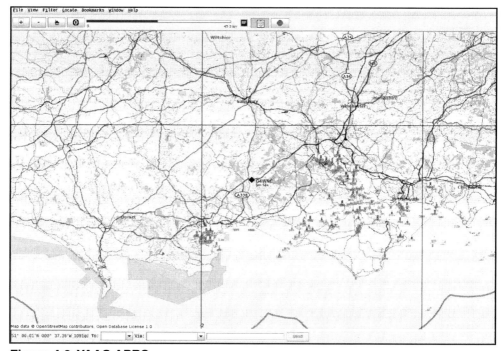

Figure 4-9: YAAC APRS screen.

1. Open your browser to navigate to: http://www.ka2ddo.org/ka2ddo/ YAAC.html
2. Download the latest version
3. Open a terminal session and let's start by installing the prerequisites:

```
sudo apt install -y openjdk-8-jre librxtx-java
```

4. Now we can install the YAAC software:

```
cd ~
mkdir yaac
cd yaac
unzip ../Downloads/YAAC.zip
```

Configuring YAAC: That completes the installation, so we can move on to the configuration. Begin by starting Direwolf because we need that running so that YAAC can connect to it. You can now run YAAC by changing to the yaac directory (cd ~/yaac/) and entering:

```
java –Xmx512m –jar YAAC.jar
```

This line warrants some explanation! The first command (java) starts the Java runtime engine whilst -Xmx512m sets the heap memory to 512MB. This is required so that YAAC can import new map data. The -jar option tells the Java engine that we want to run a .jar file and finally we supply the filename YAAC.jar.

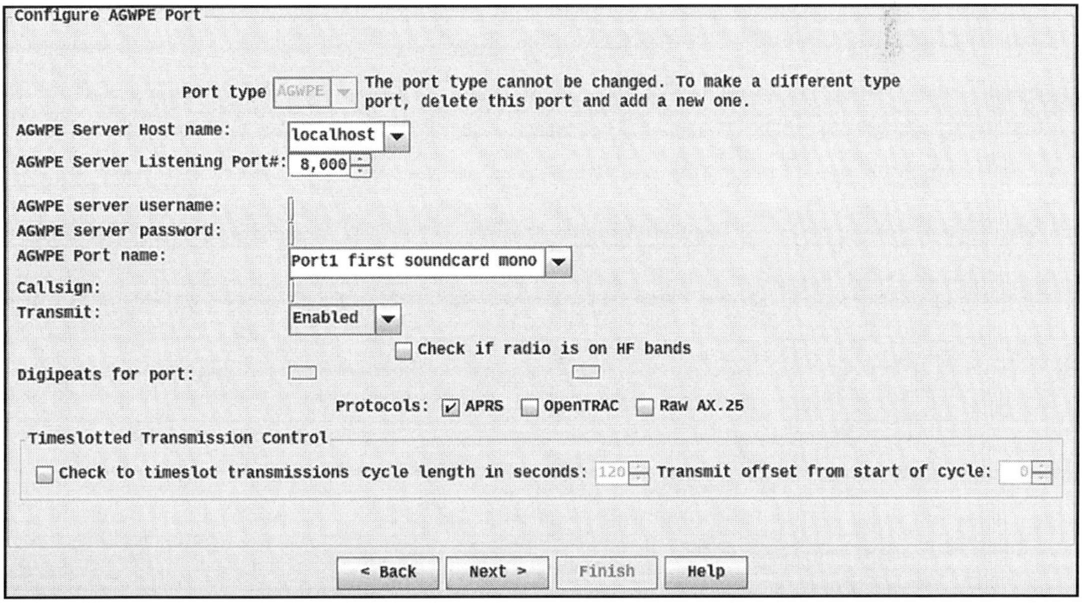

Figure 4-10: YAAC Configuration.

The first time you run YAAC it will prompt you to use the configuration wizard and I recommend using the wizard unless you are already familiar with YAAC. Follow the wizard's prompts and enter your station details, it is common practice to add a suffix to your call as you may be operating on different bands simultaneously, e.g. running APRS whilst operating a data mode on HF, WSPR, etc. In the first page of the YAAC wizard you need to enter your callsign in the top box but select your suffix from the drop-down menu, according to the type of station you're running. On the next page, tick the appropriate boxes to indicate your station type and on the following page enter your location information. When you get to the 'Add and Configure Interfaces' section, you should choose 'Add an AGWPE port and accept the defaults **Figure 4-10** (previous page). That completes the configuration and you should start seeing local stations appearing on the screen in the map. One important point to note is that YAAC has been designed for use as part of an emergency network during a major disaster. In that case, Internet access may not be available, so YAAC uses locally stored map tiles and doesn't automatically download tiles for your area. However, YAAC does include an efficient manual downloader so you can retrieve maps for your area and store them locally. For operational help, YAAC has an excellent built-in help file and the author's web site also has plenty of useful support.

SDR on the Pi

Software Defined Radio (SDR) has now become standard practice for radio designers because it has so many benefits over traditional analogue filtering and frequency translation techniques. In its purest form, an SDR receiver will digitise the incoming RF signal as close as possible to the antenna. With full digitisation, the entire performance and features of the receiver are under software control. This allows for the addition of new features and modes simply by updating the software. You can also create a completely new type of receive system simply by changing the software. A good example of this flexibility can be seen in the Lime SDR transceiver development board. This transceiver hardware has a frequency range of 100kHz to 6GHz and provides dual receive and transmit channels. The function of the transceiver can be completely changed from say an amateur transceiver to a 4G mobile base station, simply by loading different software. This flexibility brings huge manufacturing cost savings because a single, versatile SDR based transceiver board can form the basis of many different products.

One of the challenges for modern SDR systems is handling the extremely high-speed data that they produce. A high-end SDR transceiver covering all the HF bands and up to 50MHz will produce a continuous data-stream of around 2Gb/s from the output of the ADC (Analogue to Digital Converter). Managing the flow of this data is difficult enough, but we also need to perform complex, real-time, calculations on that data. The standard solution is to employ an FPGA (Field Programmable Gate Array). As the name suggests, an FPGA typically contains thousands of logic gates and other useful processing blocks that can be linked together using programmable interconnects. You can visualise it as the ultimate breadboard containing all your favourite logic chips with solid-

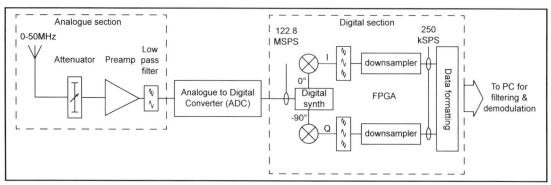

Figure 5-1: Direct Digital down-conversion block diagram.

state switches to interconnect them. In addition to their enormous flexibility, modern FPGAs are extremely fast and can be configured to parallel process many of the tasks associated with DSP (Digital Signal Processing). This makes them ideal for handling the raw data from the ADCs and down-sampling it to extract narrower bandwidth slots for filtering and demodulation, **Figure 5-1.** This process is similar to that used in a super-heterodyne, receiver, where analogue mixers and filters are used to produce a narrow-band Intermediate Frequency (IF). The transmit section can be equally challenging because the DAC (Digital to Analogue Converter) needs to be fed with high-speed data at a similar rate to the receiver.

When using the Raspberry Pi as part of an SDR receiver or transceiver, the processing power of the Pi can be a limitation. However, many enthusiasts have persevered with the challenge and we now have several excellent SDR packages that will run very well on the Pi. I'll cover these here with details of how to install them.

Raspberry Pi SDR transceivers

High Performance SDR (HPSDR) Project:
This project is run by several the leading lights in the amateur radio SDR field and, as the name suggests, is dedicated to developing high performance SDRs for amateur radio. The project has gone through several iterations and the best-known commercial outcome is the ANAN range of transceivers. The original HPSDR work was based on a modular design so that the development work could be shared across several specialist teams. Once the main designs had been completed, work commenced on a separate project (Hermes) to develop a single board SDR that consolidated the learning from the main HPSDR project. The commercial ANAN range of transceivers from Apache Labs is based on the HPSDR Hermes design, **Figure 5-2.** This is an advanced design using 16-bit sampling at 122.8MHz to provide direct digital sampling of the entire RF spectrum between LF and 55MHz. This transceiver has been designed to be controlled

via a standard Ethernet link with the final, low-bandwidth, filtering and demodulation handled in separate software running on a network-connected computer. Whilst PCs are often used to provide the final processing, it is also well within the capabilities of the Pi-3B. Thanks to the generosity of John Melton, G0ORX/N6LYT, we have PiHPSDR available as a dedicated SDR software package for the Pi. This software is very simple to install and has been designed to operate with the Pi official 7" touch screen, **Figure 5-3**. PiHPSDR is also available as a ready-built commercial product designed to work with the ANAN transceiver range. In addition to providing touch and mouse control of HPSDR rigs, the software supports several external controls and switches including a high-resolution shaft encoder for smooth manual tuning. The software works extremely well with the Pi and can support two receivers from the same SDR hardware so you can monitor any two bands between 1.8MHz and 30MHz at the same time. It can run these two receivers on all except the 384kHz bandwidth setting, which is just a little too much work for a Pi-3B.

Figure 5-2: ANAN-10, transceiver derived from the HDSDR project.

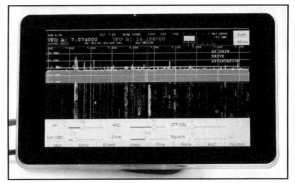

Figure 5-3: PiHPSDR running on a Pi4B.

Hermes Lite-2:

For a more modest transceiver based on the HPSDR project, the Hermes-Lite 2.0, **Figure 5-4**, is well worth a look. This has been designed as a lower cost transceiver with an RF output of 5W on all bands from 1.8MHz (Top Band) to 30MHz (10m band). At its heart, is the AD9866

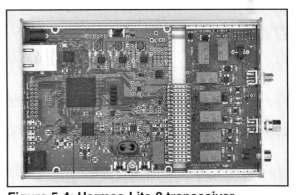

Figure 5-4: Hermes-Lite-2 transceiver.

cable modem chip that includes 12-bit ADC/DACs and facilitates which helps achieve a build cost of under $250. The Hermes-Lite 2.0 uses the HPSDR version 1 protocol for the Ethernet link, so can also be controlled by PiHPSDR, Quisk and other software. To use the Hermes-Lite 2.0 as a complete QRP transceiver, you need to add switchable low-pass filters and the N2ADR filter set has been designed specifically for the Hermes-Lite 2.0. This combination, with a Pi and 7" display, make an excellent and highly portable QRP transceiver that's ideal for hill topping or taking on holiday. At the time of writing, the Hermes-Lite 2.0 was at Build 8 and available ready assembled from Makerfabs (https://www.makerfabs. com/hermes-lite-2.html).

RadioBerry-2 SDR Hardware:

Developed by Johan Maas, PA3GSB, the RadioBerry-2 transceiver is based on the Hermes-Lite 2.0 architecture but uses a Pi to provide the Ethernet, load the FPGA and control the transceiver. The result is a complete QRP transceiver that mounts directly on top of the Pi, **Figure 5-5**. Johan has made the full design files available via his Github site, so the PCBs can be ordered from your favourite PCB fabricator. This is an advanced home-brew project as the FPGA and AD9866 chips use very narrow pin pitch with a centre pad and many of the passive components are 0603 size. However, providing you have a few basic SMD (surface mount device) tools such as a hot-air gun, temperature controlled very fine point soldering iron and tweezers, hand construction is perfectly feasible. In addition to the Pi and the RadioBerry board, you will need to add some external bandpass filtering and a PA to boost the QRPP 40mW output. In addition to Johan's dedicated software for controlling the RadioBerry transceiver, he provides emulation software so that the RadioBerry can emulate a Hermes-Lite 2.0 transceiver which opens-up a range of SDR software options that work with HPSDR Protocol 1.

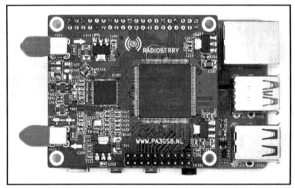

Figure 5-5: RadioBerry-2 - SDR hardware for the Raspberry Pi.

Raspberry Pi transceiver software

PiHPSDR:

This software has been designed specifically for a Pi running the official 7" touch screen monitor. The software is a free download from John Melton's, G0ORX/N6LYT Github site at: https://github.com/g0orx/pihpsdr

When you navigate to that site, you will find a link to a PDF file that contains all you need to get started. However, I've also included a step by step guide here:

1. In a terminal window navigate to the Pi home directory with: cd ~
2. Enter: wget -N https://github.com/g0orx/pihpsdr/raw/master/release/pihpsdr.tar
3. Extract the archive by entering: tar -xvf pihpsdr.tar

4. Change to the pihpsdr directory by entering: cd pihpsdr
5. Start the automatic installer by entering: ./install.sh

The install.sh manages the entire installation and even creates a desktop icon. To run the software, just double-click the desktop icon. On the initial start-up, the software will run a series of DSP tests to determine the capabilities of your Pi hardware and select the best FFT (fast Fourier transform) routines, which will then be stored in what's known as a wisdom file. PiHPSDR will then search the local network to find compatible HPSDR hardware. Once the search has completed, you will be presented with a list of all available hardware. To start PiHPSDR, highlight the desired SDR hardware and click Start. I've found that PiHPSDR works very well on a Pi-4B, 3B+ or 3A+ with a single receiver and a bandwidth of up to 192kHz. The higher, 384kHz bandwidth, with a Hermes-Lite 2.0 transceiver is a bit too much load for the processor and it can become unstable. That's not too much of a problem as 192kHz is a very practical band-width for a small screen as you can clearly identify signals from their waterfall fingerprint. PiHPSDR can also be used to monitor any two bands in the 1.8MHz to 30MHz range at the same time, by activating a second virtual receiver. When using dual receivers, you will need to reduce the receiver bandwidth and 96kHz seems to be the highest reliable rate.

If you prefer a bigger screen layout than the 800 x 480 pixels offered by PiHPSDR, I suggest you look at linHPSDR.

linHPSDR, also from John Melton, G0ORX, was developed from PiHPSDR and is intended for use with desktop PCs running Ubuntu and HPSDR com-patible hardware. Although primarily designed for Linux Ubuntu, LinHPSDR works very well on the Pi-3B running Raspbian Buster, **Figure 5-6**. As with PiHPSDR, you will need to restrict the bandwidth to 192kHz for a single receiver or 96kHz for two receivers but, with those restrictions, it works well.

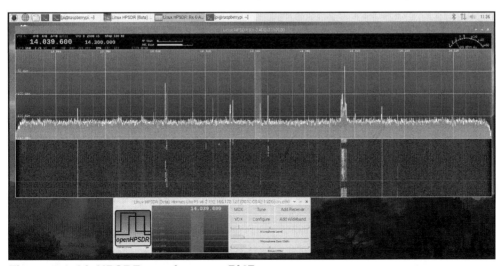

Figure 5-6: LinHPSDR running on a Pi4B

You will find an installation script for linHPSDR on my github site at: https://github.com/g4wnc/linhpsdrInstall

Installing linHPSDR:

Here is the step-by-step installation guide for linHPSDR. The installation requires a fair amount of command line work, because several of the linHPSDR dependencies are not available in the right versions from the Raspbian Buster repository. As a result, these need to be built from source. However, you should visit the author's Github site to check the latest installation process as it may well change over time. Because the installation involves a lot of command line work, I've broken it down into steps. I have also produced an installation script that available for download from my github site at: https://github.com/g4wnc/linhpsdrInstall.

Step 1 - Install the prerequisites from the Raspbian Buster repository. Open a terminal session (Ctl-Alt-T) and enter the following:

```
sudo apt install -y pulseaudio pavucontrol libpulse-dev \

cmake libusb-1.0-0-dev \

libfftw3-dev libfftw3-3 libgtk-3-dev \

libsoapysdr-dev libsoapysdr0.6
```

Step 2 - Build libsoundio from source. This is used to aid audio routing in linHPSDR. In the terminal session enter the following sequence of commands:

```
cd ~

git clone https://github.com/andrewrk/libsoundio.git

cd libsoundio

mkdir build

cd build

cmake ..

make

sudo make install
```

Step 3 - Build wdsp from source. WDSP is an open source digital signal processing library for use in SDRs.

```
cd ~

git clone https://github.com/g0orx/wdsp.git

cd wdsp
```

```
make

sudo make install
```

Step 4 - Finally, we can install linHPSDR by entering the following:

```
cd ~

git clone https://github.com/g0orx/linhpsdr.git

cd linhpsdr

make

sudo make install
```

That completes the software installation, but you will also need to add a USB sound card if you want the Pi to produce a local audio output.

Running linHPSDR:

Once installation completes, go to the Pi menu button – click on Other and you should see linHPSDR listed. When started for the first time, linHPSDR will run a series of FFT (fast Fourier transform) tests to establish the optimum code blocks for your Pi. This is an essential operation that will take a few minutes to run. When the tests have completed, the results are stored in a wisdom file that linHPSDR refers to every time it starts. As part of its start-up initialisation, linHPSDR also probes the local network looking for HPSDR compatible hardware. The probe results are shown as a list of available devices. To start the SDR, select one of the listed SDR hardware devices and click the start button. You will see two linHPSDR panels open one is the main FFT display and the other is the control panel **Figure 5-7**. On the FFT panel you will see a combined spectrum and waterfall display along with an S-meter and many of the common operational controls. This panel can be resized to suit your screen layout and the spectrum/ waterfall split can also be moved using the mouse. As with most SDR's, LinHPSDR supports click-tuning on the spectrum display along with fine tuning using the mouse wheel. The second, smaller, Control panel provides access to the SDR configuration panel where you can add receivers and a full spectrum display. When using a Pi, you need to be cautious with processor

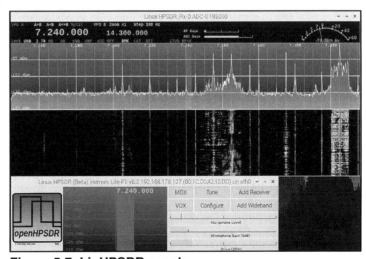

Figure 5-7: LinHPSDR panels.

loading when using multiple receivers or a full spectrum display. If you notice any audio stuttering or the display freezes, you will need to reduce the load by dropping the sample-rate. The sample rate control can be found by selecting the Configure button and then the Radio tab. At the top of that panel, you will see the radio name with the filter selection and the sample rate. To support two receivers, you will need to drop the rate to 96,000 or even 48,000 if you're running other software such as a data modes decoder. When first run, you may find the spectrum and waterfall displays are blank. This is because their settings need to be configured to match your SDR. In the RX-0 tab of the Configuration panel, you will find the settings for both the panadapter spectrum display and the waterfall. To optimise the displays, you will have to adjust the high and low sliders. One point to note in the waterfall panel is the Waterfall Automatic tick-box. This must be unticked if you want to manually adjust the waterfall levels. All the sliders operate in real-time, so you can watch the display as you adjust the sliders to get the desired display.

When you start using LinHPSDR, you will probably find there is no audio from the Pi. This is because the software assumes you are using a network connected SDR that may well have its own audio amplifier and speaker. If you're using LinHPSDR with a Hermes or similar unit, you will need to activate the local audio. This is easily done as follows:

1. In the linHPSDR control panel select Configure
2. In the Radio tab, select Audio - PULSEAUDIO and leave the Backend blank
3. Select the RX0 tab
4. In the Audio section, use the drop-down menu to choose your USB soundcard
5. Just above the card selection tick the box marked Local Audio

You should now be able to hear signs of life from the output of your soundcard through whatever audio device you have connected (headphones, amplified speakers etc). One other point to watch, is the volume control. There are two controls in play that are effectively connected in series. The first is in LinHPSDR and labelled as 'AF Gain', whilst the other is the Pi's master volume control that's accessed via the speaker icon on the top bar of the desktop. To access the Pi volume control, first right-click on the speaker icon (top-right of screen) and make sure your USB sound card is the selected sound device. Once that is done, you can left click the speaker icon to access the volume slider. I recommend leaving the Pi volume close to maximum and relying on the LinHPSDR AF gain control to adjust the volume. Most of the rest of the SDR configuration is easy to navigate but you will also find plenty of help available via the Internet.

Pi and LinHPSDR - data modes terminal

Combining one of the Hermes architecture SDRs with data mode software makes an ideal match. In particular, the Hermes Lite-2 or RadioBerry-2 transceivers have the potential to make a very compact data mode station that would be idea for portable or holiday operation. As both PiHPSDR and LinHPSDR run very efficient code, there is enough spare processing capacity on the Pi 3B (or faster models) to run popular data modes software such as WSJT-X, FLDIGI and QSSTV. One important point to note is that the Pi 7" touch screen or similar size displays are not suitable for use with these popular data modes packages. This is because these programs are designed for desktop computers that have plenty of screen real estate. When run with a Pi 7" or smaller display, the program display will overflow the screen and buttons critical for program operation will be inaccessible. In my experience, 10.1" HD displays are the minimum size that can be used with these programs. That still makes the Pi an excellent foundation for a compact SDR and data mode terminal.

Working with Data Mode software:

Installation of data mode software is covered elsewhere in chapter 4 dealing with popular radio applications, so please use those instructions or check the guidance on the software's author's website. When running SDR software with data mode software, we need to transfer the audio between applications as a digital stream to avoid the lossy process of converting to analogue and back to digital. In the world of PCs, Virtual Audio Cable software is usually purchased to create the looping for these audio streams. However, Linux distributions can handle audio distribution using free software from the standard repositories. To keep the audio routing simple, I suggest you use LinHPSDR software because this uses the popular PulseAudio sound server that greatly simplifies audio routing. The PulseAudio server is not currently included in the standard Raspbian distribution but is installed as one of the prerequisites with LinHPSDR. In addition to the sound server, we also need the PulseAudio Volume Control. This is a graphic application that provides visibility of all the active audio streams, along with the means to interconnect them. Installing the PulseAudio Volume Control can be done with a single command line in a terminal, as follows:

```
sudo apt install -y pavucontrol
```

Once installed, the volume control can be found in the Pi menu under Sound & Video. For the next step we need to create a couple of virtual sound devices that will carry our digital audio. There are various ways to do this, but the simplest is to create a couple of null sinks. These are dummy software devices that can be used to receive digital audio streams. In this case, you need to create two null sinks, one for the receive audio and the other for the transmit. To create and name the sinks, you need to make a new config file. This config file needs to be saved with the following location and name

~/.config/pulse/default.pa

Here's a step-by-step guide:

1. Open a terminal session (Ctl-Alt-T)
2. Open or create a new file with:

```
sudo nano ~/.config/pulse/default.pa
```

3. Enter the following lines into the file:

```
include /etc/pulse/default.pa

load-module module-null-sink sink_name=HPSDRrx sink_
properties="device.description='Receive  Audio'"

load-module module-null-sink sink_name=HPSDRtx sink_

properties="device.description='Transmit Audio'"
```

4. NB: Both 'load-module' entries occupy a line each.
5. When you've finished typing, press Ctl-X followed by Y and Enter to save and close the file.
6. For the changes to take effect, you need to restart the PulseAudio server either by rebooting the Pi or entering: pulseaudio -k

You can now check that the null-sinks have been created by running the PulseAudio Volume Control and clicking on the Output Devices tab. Here you should see two new devices named 'Receive Audio' and 'Transmit Audio'. If they are missing, go back to the config file and check for typos. If all is well with the sinks, you can move on to setup the routing. Here's a step-by-step guide:

1. Start PulseAudio volume control, linHPSDR and WSJT-X.
2. In linHPSDR click the Configure button and select the RX-0 tab.
3. In the Audio panel use the drop-down box and select Receive Audio and click the Local Audio box.
4. Select the TX tab in linHPSDR and set the microphone to Monitor Transmit audio and tick the Local Microphone box.
5. Close the linHPSDR Configure panel.
6. Switch to PulseAudio volume control and select the playback tab.
7. You should see linHPSDR RX-0 showing as a playback stream. This is the receive audio and needs to be routed to Receive audio. Click the box on the right and select Receive audio.
8. Click the Tune button in WSJT-X and a you should see a new stream appear in PulseAudio volume control with a name beginning 'QtPulseAudio:…'. That is the transmit audio stream from WSJT-X and needs to be routed to Transmit audio using the box on the right of that panel.
9. Switch to WSJT-X Settings - Audio tab.
10. Set sound card Input to HPSDRrx.monitor and sound card Output to HPSDRtx.

That completes the audio routing and you are now set to operate WSJT-X

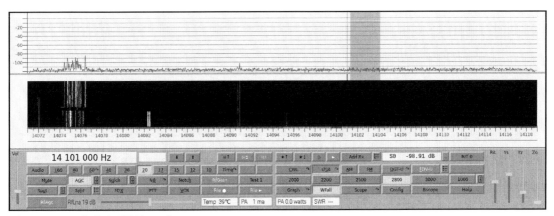

Figure 5-8: Quisk SDR main screen.

using VOX Tx/Rx switching with linHPSDR. For more detailed operating guidance for the WSJT-X suite of programs, please see the comprehensive user guide that's available on the WSJT-X website at: https://physics.princeton.edu/pulsar/k1jt/wsjtx.html

Quisk

Another popular choice for use with SoftRock and Hermes based SDR transceivers is Quisk, **Figure 5-8**. This is a cross-platform SDR transceiver application written in Python by James Ahlstrom, N2ADR. The software is highly configurable and runs well on a Pi 3B. Quisk is distributed via the PyPi Python Package Repository and is easily installed using the Python PIP utility. Installation begins with installation of the prerequisites by entering the following two lines of code in a terminal session:

```
sudo apt install -y python-wxgtk3.0 libfftw3-dev libasound2-
dev portaudio19-dev libpulse-dev

sudo apt install -y libpython2.7-dev python-usb python-
setuptools python-pip
```

Once those installations have finished, Quisk can be installed using the PIP tool as follows:

```
sudo -H pip install --upgrade quisk
```

As you can probably guess, that same command can be used to upgrade Quisk at a later date if needed. Once the software is installed, you can run it by entering quisk (NB: all lower case) in a terminal session. To configure Quisk for your SDR hardware, you start with the Config button on the main display which will activate the main configuration panel. This may seem overwhelming at first sight because this panel provides access to just about all the available Quisk settings. The default settings leave Quisk expecting to see a SoftRock device connected to the soundcard. Unless you're using a SoftRock the first

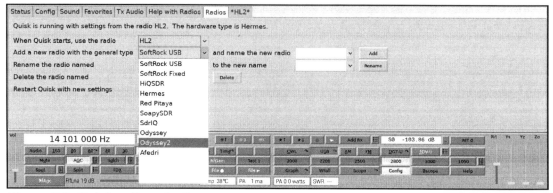

Figure 5-9: Quisk radio selection.

task is to add your radio using the Radio tab. Here's a simple guide:

1. Open the drop-down menu marked 'Add a new radio ….' and select your radio, **Figure 5-9**.
2. Move to the next drop-down on the right and assign your radio a name then click the Add button.
3. Now move back up to the first item and set Quisk to use your newly added radio when it starts.
4. During configuration a new tab should have appeared on the Configuration panel displaying the radio name you've just added. This is where you set the specific configuration for that radio.

The specific configuration is device dependent, so you'll need to check the required settings with your user manual. You may also find that there are tutorial videos available on YouTube that can help. The Hermes Lite-2 is very well provided for with dedicated YouTube tutorials for the Hermes Lite-2 and Quisk. These can be easily found using Google. When you've finished configuring your device, go back to the Radio tab and hit the restart Quisk button to restart the program with all the new settings. For more detailed help on configuring and using Quisk, I recommend heading over to the author's website at:

http://james.ahlstrom.name/quisk/docs.html. You will also find Web tutorials and videos available to help with all the popular SDR hardware.

Quisk is one of my favourite applications for controlling my Hermes Lite-2 and RadioBerry-2 transceivers because it has a very clear display and plenty of customisation options. The range of supported SDR hardware has recently been extended to include SoapySDR support. This is an important addition because it opens-up Quisk, and the Pi to a larger number of SDR hardware devices. However, you still need to be mindful of the limited processing power. If you see signs of audio stuttering or the FFT displays freezing, you will need to reduce the processor load and the simplest way to do that is to reduce the sample rate.

Quisk and data modes software

Quisk has inbuilt provision for creating loopback audio devices so audio signals can be routed directly to data modes software as well as a local USB sound card for audio monitoring. The first step is to open the Quisk Configure panel, choose the Audio tab and set the Radio Sound Output, Microphone Input, External Digital Input and External Digital Output to use the default Pulse device. Adding these entries causes Quisk to automatically create the loopback devices we need next time it starts. To continue the configuration close and restart Quisk.

In order to use the new digital devices, you need to select the Digital mode in Quisk rather than USB. The digital mode to use is DGT-U, ie digital upper sideband. The other vital point is to make sure you start Quisk before you run your data mode software. This is important because the Quisk digital input and output devices only exist whilst the program is running and most data mode software packages only check for sound devices during start up. Therefore, if you start the data mode software first, it won't be able to find the Quisk digital outputs! The simplest way to control the audio routing is to use the PulseAudio Volume Control application. If you've not already installed this, here's how:

1. Open a terminal session (Ctl-Alt-T)
2. Enter:

```
sudo apt install -y pavucontrol
```

Once installed, you will find the volume control under the Pi menu - Sound & Video. I've shown a block diagram of the interconnections in **Figure 5-10** and

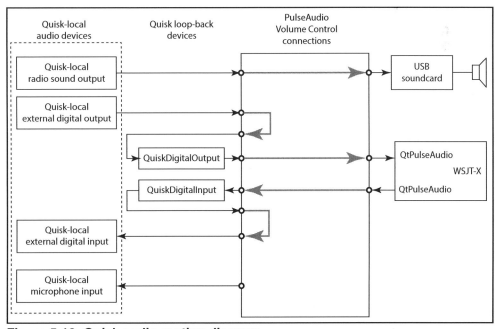

Figure 5-10: Quisk audio routing diagram.

here's a step by step guide to configuring the audio streams with WSJT-X.

1. With Quisk and WSJT-X running, DGT-U selected as the operating mode, and your USB sound card connected, open the WSJT-X Settings and select the Audio tab.
2. Set the Input to QuiskDigitalOutput monitor and set the Output to QuiskDigitalOutput.
3. Next, open the PulseAudio volume control and select the Playback tab. You should see two active streams running: 'Quisk-local Radio Sound Output on' and 'Quisk-local External Digital Output on'
4. To the right of these two streams you will see a drop-down menu where you can set the destination for these streams. Use this menu to set Radio Sound Output to your USB sound card and the External Digital Output to QuiskDigitalOutput.
5. Before leaving the Playback tab connect your rig to a dummy load and press the tune button in WSJT-X. You should see a new QtPulseAudio stream appear at the bottom of the Playback tab. This is the transmit audio stream from WSJT-X and needs to be set to Quisk-DigitalInput
6. Select the Recording tab and set the Quisk-local External Digital Input to Monitor of. QuiskDigitalInput. Also, on the Recording tab, set the QtPulseAudio stream to Monitor of QuiskDigitalOutput.

That completes the audio routing and the settings will be remembered for future sessions. Just remember to always start Quisk before the data mode software. The same process can be used to configure other data mode software.

Raspberry Pi SDR receive only software

In addition to the full transceive software I've covered so far, there are several receive only SDR applications that work well on the Pi. The most well established is Gqrx, which is based on the GNU Radio libraries.

Gqrx on the Pi: Gqrx is a versatile SDR package created by Alexandru Csete, OZ9AEC that uses the popular GNU Radio suite of libraries to provide the digital signal processing (DSP) blocks and Qt5 for the Graphic User Interface (GUI), **Figure 5-11**. As with all SDRs, Gqrx requires significant processor resources and has only really become practical for use on a Raspberry Pi since the introduction of the Pi-3B. I recommend using the fastest Pi model available and the original Pi-3B is the minimum acceptable specification. Gqrx works with many of the popular SDR hardware systems and below is the list of hardware that was supported at the time of writing.

- FUNcube Dongle Pro
- FUNcube Dongle Pro+
- Universal Software Radio Peripheral (USRP)
- RTL-SDR - USB and TCP connections

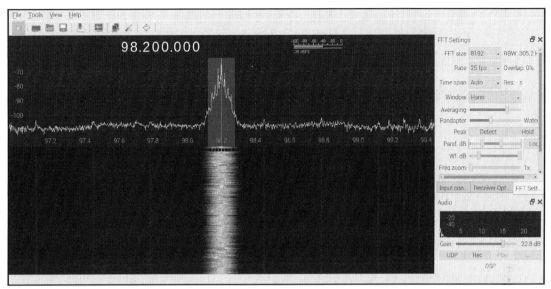

Figure 5-11: GQRX main screen.

- HackRF Jawbreaker
- RFspace SDR-IQ, SDR-IP and NetSDR
- Airspy
- Airspy HF+
- Lime SDR
- Pluto SDR
- Nuand BladeRF
- SDRplay
- I/Q file source

Installing Gqrx:
To install Gqrx, you will need an Internet connected Pi-3B or later with a keyboard, mouse and monitor. Alternatively, you can use a headless connection from another computer. You will also need to connect one of the supported SDRs and a USB soundcard. I recommend starting with the latest Raspbian image.

Here's a step-by-step guide to installation:

1. Open a terminal session (Ctl-Alt-T).
2. Enter:
```
sudo apt install -y gnuradio libvolk1-bin libusb-1.0-0
gr-iqbal
```
3. Enter:
```
sudo apt install -y qt5-default libqt5svg5 libportaudio2
```

4. Open a browser and navigate to http://gqrx.dk/download
5. Click on the Raspberry Pi-3 link to access the Gqrx for Raspberry Pi page and click the Gqrx SDR download link. This will download the compressed archive and save it in the Downloads folder.
6. Open a terminal session on the Pi (Ctl-Alt-T)
7. The next step is to create a new folder for the unpacked archive by entering:

```
mkdir ~/gqrx
```

NB: The ~ symbol is a short-cut to your home directory, ie /home/pi

8. Now we can change to the new directory with: cd ~/gqrx
9. To extract the archive to the new gqrx folder enter the following. NB: Update the file name to match the downloaded file:

```
sudo tar -xvf ~/Downloads/gqrx-sdr-2.11.5-linux-rpi3.
tar.xz --strip-components=1
```

10. Installing the User Device Rules (Udev rules) is next and this informs the Linux kernel how to handle the SDR hardware. To copy the Udev drivers, enter:

```
sudo cp ~/gqrx/udev/*.rules /etc/udev/rules.d
```

Finally, we need to run the Volk profiler that's used to select the optimum DSP code for your processor. It does this by executing several complex calculations and measuring the execution time. This only needs to be run once and is started with the following command:

```
sudo volk_profile
```

Running Gqrx:

We are now ready to run Gqrx but before we do, you must have your SDR hardware and a USB sound card connected to the Pi. It's important to connect these before you start Gqrx, because the program checks for connected devices during the start-up. As a result, any device connected after Gqrx is running may not be properly detected. To run Gqrx, open the File Manager, navigate to the gqrx folder and double-click on the gqrx file. This will give an option to Execute or Execute in terminal. Both options will start the program but if you choose Execute in Terminal, a terminal widow will open, and you will be able to see the system messages output by Gqrx. This is mainly of use if you are having problems, as the messages will give you some pointers as to the root cause. At the time of writing, Gqrx works well on all the narrow-band modes but often struggles with wideband reception such as Stereo FM. This shows itself as stuttering or choppy audio. The overcome this, you will need to reduce the processor loading by using the FFT tab to reduce the frame rate, FFT size, etc. The processor load also depends very much on the connected device and you should use the minimum IQ bandwidth. For those interested in LF to HF, the Airspy HF+ series of receivers are ideal for use with Gqrx. This is because they use a relatively narrow IQ bandwidth of 786kHz, which results in a lower processor loading. The Airspy HF+ series are also one of the best receivers around and make use of the latest advances in SDR technology.

Gqrx on the Pi has had an oddity with AM reception where you may need to select the AM options (three dots …) and uncheck the DCR box.

Linrad

Linrad is an advanced SDR software package developed by Leif Asbrink, SM5BSZ that can be used on multiple platforms, including the Raspberry Pi, **Figure 5-12**. When correctly configured, Linrad uses the limited resources of the Pi very ef- ficiently. Linrad is also particularly good at resolving very weak signals. At the heart of Linrad's excellent performance, is the freedom given to the user to ad- just most of the SDR parameters. Whilst that flexibility is very welcome, it does require a sound knowledge of SDR technology on the part of the user. Despite this complexity, it is still possible to obtain excellent performance from Linrad thanks to other enthusiasts sharing their optimised settings online. Leif has also provided plenty of video tutorials on his YouTube channel: SM5BSZ.

Installing Linrad: Linrad needs to be installed from source as there are no pre-compiled binaries available for the Raspberry Pi. Links to the source code and installation instructions can be found on Leif's site here: http://sm5bsz.com/ linuxdsp/linrad.htm. I'll also run through the installation process with this step-by- step guide and have produced an install script that can be found on my github site at: https://github.com/g4wnc. The first step is to install a few supporting libraries. You may find some of these already exist on your Pi, in which case they will be checked to make sure they are the latest available.

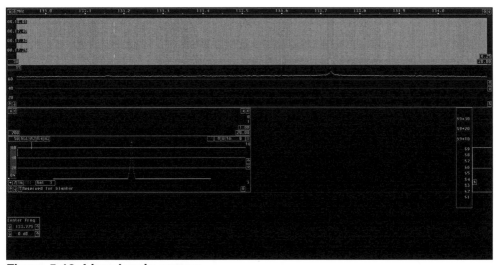

Figure 5-12: Linrad main screen.

1. Open a terminal session and enter the following:

```
sudo apt install -y subversion libx11-dev libxext-dev
libusb-1.0-0-dev libusb-dev cmake libportaudio-dev
```

2. With the prerequisites done, we can now download the latest source code with these commands:

```
cd ~
```

```
svn checkout https://svn.code.sf.net/p/linrad/code/
trunk linrad
```

3. You will probably see a failure warning, but we don't need to worry about that for now. At this point, the source code has been downloaded into the Linrad directory so we can start the installation.

4. Change to the Linrad directory with:

```
cd ~/linrad
```

5. Start the build process by typing:

```
./configure
```

The final step should complete with a message stating a 'Normal end. You can now run make'. However, immediately above this message you should see some red text with a list of missing or not working libraries (non-fatal). This is normal. These are the optional libraries and hardware drivers and you will need to install to support the specific SDR hardware you want to use. The Linrad configure script provides some excellent guidance on how to install these drivers. You can access this help by entering:

```
sudo ./configure --with-help
```

This will again list all the missing libraries but will also give the commands required to install those libraries. One point to note here is that Leif assumes you are entering these commands as a super-user with enhanced permissions. I suggest you open a second terminal session and use the command: sudo su to give the second session enhanced root permissions. You can then copy and paste Leif's installation instructions into the second terminal screen. You can check that Linrad can see the new drivers by running configure again and checking the missing libraries list.

With all the requirements satisfied, we can now complete the build process. For our purposes, we want the X-Windows version of Linrad so we can use a graphic interface. Here is the command:

```
sudo make xlinrad
```

This will take some time to complete, so be patient. Once complete, you can run Linrad from the terminal by moving to the Linrad directory with:

```
cd ~/linrad
```

Next start Linrad with:

```
sudo ./xlinrad
```

When the program starts, you will be presented with some basic configuration steps and I suggest you begin with the following replies: Select your graphics from A to C. Enter A.

The next choice is to select the Global parameters and I suggest you start with Newcomer mode by entering N.

Next you can specify a screen size in pixels or %. I suggest responding n for percentage and then answer 80% to the width and height prompts.

Next you will be presented with the newcomer mode screen where you need to select the sound card by pressing: U followed by 0 to select ALSA. The next step is to select your SDR hardware (receiver input). Press A and you will be presented with a list of all the hardware supported by Linrad. NB: You can only use the hardware that you installed during the build process. If you want to add a new SDR device, you must install the drivers and then go back to the Linrad directory and re-run configure followed by: sudo make xlinrad.

Choose your installed SDR from the alphabetically sorted list. Linrad will check that the device is available and give you the option to adjust some of the device specific parameters. I suggest you enter the default values at this point. The next task is to set the audio output device for Linrad by pressing B. This will give you the option to use PortAudio, answer N to this. You should then see a list of all the available sound devices and you will probably find your USB sound card at the bottom of the list, so select that. That completes the basic configuration and you can press X to return to the main menu. This will give you a prompt to save the parameters when you get to the main menu. Press W to save the parameters and the screen will display those parameters. At this point the basic configuration is complete and you can start using Linrad. As I mentioned at the beginning, Linrad is an excellent SDR software package but it has a very steep learning curve, so you need to be prepared to spend some time learning how to use it. There are plenty of guides on the web and I suggest joining the Linrad support group on Google Groups. You will also find a very helpful Linrad Data Bank at:

http://www.nitehawk.com/linrad_dat/. This contains links to an excellent range of Linrad guides. Probably the most useful document for those new to Linrad is the Linrad Installation & Configuration User Guide by Gaëtan Horlin, ON4KHG. Although this 52-page guide is based on a Windows installation most of the document focuses on configuration and that is common for Windows and Linux installations. One other very useful document is Linrad Screen Controls by Joe Taylor, K1JT. This 9-page document is a very helpful reference to all the screen controls.

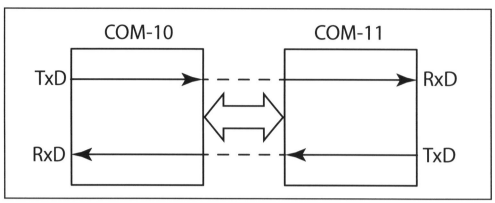

Figure 5-13: Socat virtual COM port configuration.

CAT rig control and virtual COM ports

As we move to SDR for more of our radio activities, there is a growing need to interconnect software so that commands and other information can be shared between programs. A typical example would be a data modes operator that needs to control the transceiver frequency from inside a program, such as WSJT-X. Another example is a logging program that retrieves frequency and mode information directly from the rig. The most common way to handle this information exchange is to use a serial data link. These links are loosely based around the RS-232 standard that was introduced in the 1960's to handle communications between computers and data modems. In today's computing, dominated by Windows, these serial connections are known as COM ports. When using CAT control with a stand-alone rig, the link between the rig and the computer normally comprises a dedicated cable that is fitted with a serial to USB converter. When this cable is plugged into the computer, the appropriate driver software is loaded, and the link is automatically assigned a COM port number. When using Linux, a similar process occurs but the serial connection is allocated a /dev/tty name, which derives from its original purpose that was to connect a teletype machine. As soon as we introduce SDR based radios into a radio station we have the potential to handle the data exchange entirely in software, thus avoiding the dedicated USB to serial cable. However, the rig and the software are expecting to exchange data using a serial connection. The solution is to create virtual serial ports to transport the data between programs. The common way to do this is use a small program to create a pair of software interconnected /dev/tty ports, **Figure 5-13**. There are many ways to create virtual serial ports, but my favourite program for this functionality is SOCAT. SOCAT is a very useful and free utility that can be used to create all manner of interconnected byte streams.

Let's begin by installing SOCAT. The version in the Pi repository is fine for our purposes, so use the following command to install it:

```
sudo apt install -y socat.
```

Once the installation has completed, a pair of interconnected serial ports can be created with the following single line command:

```
sudo socat PTY,link=/dev/ttyS10 PTY,link=/dev/ttyS11
```

This will create two new, interconnected, ports called /dev/ttyS10 and /dev/ttyS11. You can check that these exist by listing all the tty devices with this command:

```
ls /dev/tty*
```

The new devices should show as /dev/ttyS10 and /dev/ttyS11. Whilst the single-line command to create the serial ports is simple enough we don't want to enter this every time the Pi reboots. Whilst that works ok, we really need the extra ports to be automatically created when the Pi boots. We can do that very easily by making use the Systemd service to automatically run the command as a service. In addition to automatically creating the desired ports Systemd can be used to check their status and to disable them if necessary. Configuring a program to be called by Systemd is very easy and begins by creating a dedicated .service file that contains details of how we want the service to run. Here's how to create a new .service file:

1. Open a terminal session (Ctl-Atl-T) and enter the following:

   ```
   sudo nano /etc/systemd/system/CATports.service
   ```

2. This will create a new service file called CATports.service and open it in the Nano editor.

3. Populate the file with the following. NB: Be very careful to get the capitalisation right:

   ```
   [Unit]
   Description=Virtual serial port pair
   [Service]
   ExecStart=/usr/bin/socat PTY,link=/dev/ttyS10 PTY,link=/dev/ttyS11
   Restart=always
   [Install]
   WantedBy=multi-user.target
   ```

4. Press Ctl-X followed by Y then Enter to save and close the file.

With the service file created, we can start the service by entering: sudo systemctl start CATports. This should return without error and we can check that the ports have been created by entering:

```
ls /dev/tty*
```

This will list all the tty ports and you should find ttyS10 and ttyS11 are present. You can also check the status of the service by entering:

```
systemctl status CATports
```

This should produce a status report and, if you don't see the appropriate results, the most common mistake is a typo in the service file. Re-open that file and check it very carefully, taking special care to check the capitalisation. If everything is working as expected, you can set the service to automatically start at boot by entering the following:

```
sudo systemctl enable CATports
```

When it comes to using the ports, you can visualise their functionality as a serial cable where one end is called /dev/ttyS10 and the other end is /dev/ttyS11. In the SDR CAT settings, you would choose /dev/ttyS10 whilst in the data modes program choose /dev/ttyS11.

Summary

In this chapter I have shown that the Pi is a useful processing core for a wide range of SDR radio applications. The low-cost transceiver hardware derived from the HPSDR Hermes project is ideally suited for use with the Pi and makes home construction of a complete direct digital sampling SDR transceiver eminently practical. Whilst it's important to bear in mind the processing limitations of the Pi, it can comfortably handle the bandwidths typically used on the LF-HF bands and narrow-band communications on higher bands.

6

Pi Linux

The Pi has always relied on Linux for its operating system and there are several reasons for this. First and foremost, Linux is an open source operating system that means it is free of charge to the end user. In addition, there is a massive support community that can help with any problems. The attraction of Linux is further enhanced by the availability of a huge range of free software. This includes Office suites that can work with all the common Microsoft Office™ applications plus web browsers, Programming IDEs and much more. Particularly important when using the Pi in education is the vast collection of free software libraries that are available. Partnering the Pi with Linux makes it an excellent learning tool as well as a very useful development platform.

Linux distributions

Whist we use the generic name Linux to describe the Pi operating system, Linux comes in many flavours. Linux itself is just the kernel of the operating system that manages the communications between all the hardware components of the computer. This kernel is usually supplemented by a bootloader to get the machine started, plus a shell for communicating with the kernel, a graphic server and a desktop environment to provide the familiar Graphic User Interface (GUI). There are many ways to supplement the Linux kernel to make a complete operating system and these are called Linux distributions. The Raspberry Pi has its own distribution known as Raspbian. The name, Raspbian is a portmanteau of the popular Debian distribution and the Raspberry Pi. You may have noticed that each version of Raspbian is given a name such as Wheezy, Jessie, Stretch and Buster. If you haven't already guessed, the names are based on characters from the Toy Story movies!

Whilst Linux is undoubtedly the right operating system for the Pi, those moving from Windows environments often struggle to get to grips with the differences. The Pi team have done some great work to smooth the transition by creating the PIXEL desktop that's included in the Raspbian distribution of Linux. This provides a GUI that lets the user navigate the file system and the Internet using familiar controls. However, most Pi users will progress to using the Linux command line for many activities as, once learnt, it is a very fast and powerful way to get things done. Even if you are intending to use mainly GUI based applications, some knowledge of common commands is essential. In this chapter, I've gathered together a selection of commands and techniques that you may find useful as you become more familiar with your Raspberry Pi.

Installing Linux

I've covered the installation in detail in chapter 3 Pi Projects.

Updating Linux

The current, official, Raspbian desktop versions include a helpful setup wizard that runs immediately after the first boot. This steers you through the initial setup and triggers a system update. For those that have skipped the wizard, or are using the Lite version, I strongly recommend updating the operating system before starting on a new project. The update is just a case of entering the following at the command line:

```
apt update && sudo apt upgrade -y && reboot
```

This is three commands written on the same line with the double ampersand (&&) used to separate them. Because the 'upgrade' command requires administrator level permissions, it is preceded with sudo. The first command updates the list of available files in the software repository, whilst the upgrade command starts the download and installs any updated software. Finally, reboot, simply restarts the computer. NB: When you combine commands with &&, the commands after the && will only execute if those before && completed successfully.

Backing-up your SD card

Once you have your fully updated system on your SD card ready to go, it's worth making a backup copy. The tool for this is built into the operating system and available via the desktop, **Figure 6-1**. The backup is very flexible and can be stored on another SD card connected via a USB SD card writer or can be written to a USB memory

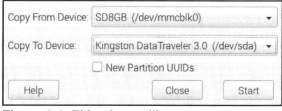

Figure 6-1: Pi backup utility.

stick. The only stipulation being that the backup storage device has the same or greater capacity than the existing Pi SD card. When copying to an SD card, the resulting card is bootable and can be plugged straight into the Pi.

When working on a new project, it's always worth having a back-up or two of an updated operating system. If you get in a pickle with conflicting software or muddled settings, you can just plug-in a new SD card and start again without having to repeat the download and update process.

Here's the step by step process:

1. From the Pi menu choose Accessories – SD Card Copier.
2. In the panel that opens, set the Copy From Device to the on-board SD card (/dev/mmcblk0).
3. Set the Copy To Device to your backup storage device. This will probably be (/dev/sda).
4. Click Start.

The copy will take around 15 minutes to complete, so be patient.

Raspberry Pi security

One of the reasons Linux is used extensively in server farms and business computing, is its inherent security. At the core of that security is the way account privileges are allocated. Whereas Windows users often have administrator access by default, Linux users are given much lower-level privileges. For example, in Raspbian, the Pi user can only change files in the Pi home directory. That makes it far more difficult for a malicious file to do any serious damage. However, the main security weakness of the Raspberry Pi is the use of a common username and password combination, pi/raspberry. Whilst this was done to help new users get started, it could provide an easy route for a hacker to access your Pi when it's exposed to the Internet. The solution is simply to change the Pi password to something more secure. The password can be changed from the desktop using the following steps:

1. From the Pi menu choose - Preferences - Raspberry Pi Configuration.
2. In the System tab, click Change Password, enter your new password twice and click OK.
3. Make sure you remember or record your password as it cannot be retrieved.

For recovering from a lost password, please refer to the Troubleshooting chapter at the end of this book.

If you have an application that you feel requires more protection, I suggest you refer to the Pi Foundation's guide to security that you can find via the following link:

https://www.raspberrypi.org/documentation/configuration/security.md

This will guide you through some advanced suggestions for securing your Pi.

Linux compressed files

Once you start experimenting with your Pi, you will undoubtedly encounter software that's packaged using files with a .tar suffix. These are commonly known as tarballs. Whilst the zip format is the most common file compression system employed in Windows, the Linux community normally use tarballs for file archives. The name originates from its early use in tape archives (Tape ARchives). The most significant difference between zip and tar archives is the way the archive is assembled. In the Windows zip format, each file is separately compressed and then added to the zip file. As a result, each file can be individually accessed and expanded. The tar approach is different and uses a tar file to assemble the desired files and then a compression tool to compress the entire package. The difference shows when you attempt to access the files. With Windows, a double-click on the Zip file will normally show all the content files and you can view individual files. With a tarball, you must first decompress the tar before you can view its contents. In practice, there's very little difference between using zip or tarballs, because most extraction tools use a single command to both decompress and extract the contents of a tarball. As you might expect, there are several file compression tools available to Linux users and I've shown a few of the most common in **Table 6-1**. As you can see, the file compression method being used is indicated by its file suffix. Table 6-1 also includes an example of how to create and extract tarball archives.

Compression tool	Characteristics	Command to archive and compress a directory	Extract command
gzip	Well established and fast	tar czvf test.tar.gz directory	tar xzvf test.tar.gz
bzip2	Well established, slower than gzip, but achieves greater compression	tar cjvf test.tar.bz2 directory	tar xjvf test.tar.bz2
xz	Relatively new and 5-10 times slower than gzip or bzip2, but can achieve 10 times the compression.	tar cJvf test.tar.xz directory	tar xJvf test.tar.xz

Table 6-1: Common tarball compression tools.

How to find the IP Address of a Pi

There are many occasions when you need to know the IP address of a Pi that's connected to your local network. Here is a selection of techniques that you may find helpful.

From the Pi Desktop:

Hover your mouse over the up/down arrow or Wi-Fi icon in the top right of the desktop. This will reveal a pop-up showing the state of your Ethernet (eth0) or wireless (wlan0) connections and will include the currently assigned IP address, **Figure 6-2.** A typical example would display the following message:

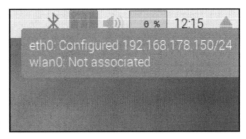

eth0: Configured 192.168.1.155/24

In this example, the IP address is 192.168.1.155.

Figure 6-2: Displaying the Pi IP address.

From the command line:
The simplest way to view the IP address from the command line is to type: hostname -I. This will return the IP address of the Pi.

There are many other commands that can be used to display the IP address and one popular option is: sudo ifconfig. The first part of the command (sudo) increases your permission level so that you can use administrator commands such as ifconfig. This is a powerful command to display the configuration details of the Pi network interfaces. In addition to showing all your Ethernet (eth0) and wireless (wlan0) interfaces, it will also report the loopback interface (lo). This interface is provided to allow software to communicate with a server running on the same Pi, without having to go out into the local network. You will see that, rather than just showing the IP address, the ifconfig command gives details of the interface performance. If you want to restrict output to a single interface, you just add that interface name to the command. Therefore, to see the configuration and performance of first Ethernet interface, you would enter: sudo ifconfig eth0.

Retaining the same IP address:
The Pi is ideally suited for use as a server for all manner of information and services. For this to work successfully, you need to know the IP address of your Pi server, but you also need that to be a permanently assigned address. Traditionally, this was done by giving the Pi a static IP address. Whilst this sounds simple enough, it can cause problems later if you or your router were to allocate that address to another device. A simpler and more reliable technique, that's available in all modern routers is to force the router to preserve the current IP address. The activation technique will vary between routers but will often be controlled by a tick-box in the router's administrator panel. In my FRITZ!Box router, it's shown as: 'Always assign this network device the same IPv4 address'. Once configured, the Dynamic Host Configuration Protocol (DHCP) server will recognise the Pi by its unique Media Access Control (MAC) identifier and allocate the IP address that's been reserved. This delegates the responsibility for all IP address management to the DHCP server in the router and thus avoids any troublesome IP conflicts.

Linux command line:
The Pi team have done a great job with the PIXEL desktop and most operations can be completed within the desktop environment. So, why bother learning the

Linux command line? Although using the command line can feel like a retrograde step at first, it's worth the effort because it can be a great time saver and provides direct access to some very powerful tools. You can also add commands to a text document and so create a more complex sequence of activities that can be run with a couple of clicks. A good example would be the update, upgrade and reboot commands I mentioned earlier. In the Programming chapter I'll show you how to write your own scripts.

Accessing the command line with LXTerminal

The Pi uses a small software package called Bash to transfer commands and information to and from the Kernel. However, when working in the PIXEL desktop, we need a GUI application to give us access to Bash. The program we need for this job is a terminal emulator and the default for the Pi is LXTerminal. You will find an icon for LXterminal on the top bar of the Pi main screen (a black rectangle with a blue line at the top). The main role of LXTerminal is to provide a screen for us to enter our commands and exchange commands and responses to and from Bash. However, most terminal emulators do a lot more than that. LXTerminal, for example, supports copy and paste, includes a buffer so you can scroll backwards, has text highlighting and more. In addition to starting LXTerminal using its icon, you can also start it by pressing function key, F4, whilst in the File Manager. This will open LXTerminal in the folder you've accessed with File Manager

Word of warning!
Once you start using the command line, you will discover the power and flex-ibility of Linux, but it does put total faith in the skills of the operator. As a result, many of the commands are executed without question. If you tell it to wipe the disk partition that holds your operating system, it will just get on and do it; no prompts, checks or do you really want to do that questions! When you ask it to do something irreversible, it's up to you to get the command right.

Windows to Linux Gotchas! Here a few Linux characteristics that can confuse new users:

1. Everything in Linux is case sensitive, so make sure you watch this, especially when using command line options.
2. Linux file names can and do use multiple periods or full-stops. For example; the file name test.v1.txt is perfectly valid in Linux. However, periods have a special meaning in some contexts, so are best avoid-ed in your own file naming. The exception being for file extensions and version ie test-1.1.txt. A common naming method for configura-tion and system files is to start the name with a period. Files begin-ning with a period are treated as hidden files and not displayed by the File Manager application or the ls command. To see these hidden files, you need to enable 'view hidden' in the File Manager or use the

-a option with the command line, ie ls -a.

3. Avoid using spaces in filenames. Linux allows spaces, but it can cause problems with some software, so is best avoided.

4. Line endings are different in Linux. Windows (DOS really) uses a carriage-return and linefeed combination to mark the end of a line, whereas Linux just uses a linefeed character. Most programmers text editors allow selection of the appropriate line ending. However, it's important to remember that a script or program written on a Windows PC probably won't run under Linux, unless you correct the line ending.

Installing software

There are a variety of techniques for installing software under Linux and I've summarised them in this section. The most popular software is normally made available through the Linux software repositories and this is the preferred source for software. This is because software in the repositories has undergone some validation checks and will be configured to install the program and configuration files in the correct system directories.

From Source: Compiling software from the source code is usually only necessary if you're accessing new software that's still in its development phase. This type of installation is quite complex because you must read the authors installation notes to prepare the installation and install the prerequisite software packages. You may also find that the author uses non-standard locations for program and configuration files. I have covered this type of installation more thoroughly in chapter 4 installing radio applications.DEB package: Next up the chain of installation methods is the DEB package, which can be recognised by the .deb filename suffix. The .deb file is a container that normally has all the program files ready compiled into binaries for use on the target system. However, it doesn't take account of any software dependencies, so these must be separately installed. The DEB package is quite sophisticated, as it can automatically upgrade or downgrade the software, whilst preserving user settings. A DEB package is very easy to install using the dpkg command, ie sudo dpk -i mysoftware

apt & apt-get. These are the two highest-level, command line, tools for installing software from a repository. Not to be confused with the acronym APT, which is the Linux Advanced Packaging Tool. Note also that apt and apt-get are two separate installation tools. The shorter named, apt, was introduced in 2014 as an easier-to-use version of apt-get and includes some additional features to aid software installation. Both applications rely on the DEB package for the target software, but they will automatically locate and install any prerequisite packages. The most common usage you'll see in tutorials and publications is: sudo apt-get install mysoftware. Although apt-get is still current, the newer apt is a better install tool as it includes a progress bar and a few other refinements. I recommend using apt as your first choice. Here's a usage example: sudo apt install mysoftware. Before installing any new software, you should always run: apt update. This will refresh the repository index to ensure you get the latest software.

GUI Package Managers: The Add/Remove Software menu entry on the Pi is an example of a GUI interface to apt and deb packages. The Pi version is called PiPackages but another popular installer you may encounter is Synaptic. These GUIs provide an easy way to install software for new users. However, you need to watch the software versions, as there are some very old and outdated packages hiding in there.

Linux command line - getting help

Table 6-2 shows a selection of Bash commands and associated options that I have found useful in my work with the Raspberry Pi. All these commands have more options than listed here and there are also many more commands available. There are several ways to get help on the use of a command. One built-in method is to type the command followed by --help. This will supply a terse but accurate use statement for the command. Alternatively, you can access the Linux manual by entering man followed by the command, eg man ls would give you the manual page for the command ls. If you'd rather see some examples using the command, then Google is your friend and a search on any Linux command will provide many useful results.

For an easy-to-use list of Bash commands and options, search for Bash cheat sheets on Google or your preferred search engine. Here's a link to a good example: https://learncodethehardway.org/unix/bash_cheat_sheet.pdf

NB: Many of these commands will need to be preceded with sudo if working outside of the Pi home directory.

Editing files from the command line

Once you start using the command line, there will be many occasions when you need to create or edit a file. This requires a simple text editor and the default for Raspbian is Nano. To create a new file, simply navigate to the directory where you want to save the file and type nano followed by the name of the file, ie nano test.txt to create a file called test.txt. If you want to create or edit a file outside of the Pi home directory, you will need to precede nano with sudo to enhance your permissions, ie sudo nano test.txt. You will also need to specify the file path. Example: To create a file called test.txt in the /etc directory you would enter:

```
sudo nano /etc/test.txt
```

When you've finished creating your file, you can close it by entering: Ctl-X followed by Y.

Command	Function	Usage Notes and examples
`--help`	Shows help	Used as a suffix for any command to view the help information.
`--version`	Shows the version of the command or software	Used as a suffix on any command or software package to report the installed version: `python --version`
`TAB key`	Triggers the auto-complete feature	To help avoid typos when entering long filenames, press the tab key and Bash will auto-complete the rest of the filename (providing it is unique)
`ls`	Lists files and folders	Displays a list of the files and directories in the current directory. Linux uses hidden files that won't show-up with ls. These files start with a decimal point. To view all files, use ls with the suffix -a. To view more details, use the -l suffix. You can also use both, ie ls -a -l
`cd`	Change directory	Change to a different directory, ie cd /etc puts you in the /etc directory.
`~`	Home (pi) directory shortcut	This is a shortcut for the pi directory. To get back to the Pi directory from anywhere in the filesystem, just enter cd ~
`mkdir`	Make a new directory	`mkdir /home/pi/test` will create a new directory called test in the pi directory.
`tree`	Displays the directory tree	Use the -a option to include hidden files and -l for more detail.
`rm`	Removes files and directories	Use the -r suffix to remove directory content as well.
`cp`	Copies files and directories	cp sourceFile destinationFile . If you want to copy a directory and keep its hierarchy use the -r option
`mv`	Move or rename files and directories	To rename a file or directory use: `mv file1.txt file2.txt` To move a file to a new location: `mv myfile.txt /home/pi/Downloads/`
`df`	Displays the disk space	Used with the -h option to see how the space is used on the current disk.
`dd`	Duplicates disks	This is a very powerful but potentially dangerous tool for copying and cloning disks. It can also be used to make disk images – see dc3dd for a better version.
`dc3dd`	Duplicates disks	This is an improved version of dd that includes progress reporting and other goodies. You need to install this separately using: `sudo apt install dc3dd` To create an image file from a disk use: `dc3dd if=/dev/sda of=disk.img`
`cat`	Text file command	A very powerful tool used to display, combine and create new text files. To view a text file on the screen use: cat mytext.txt. To combine two or more text files into a new file use: `cat file1 file2 > file3` To append text from one file to another use: `cat file1 >> file2`
`echo`	Writes to the standard output (normally the screen)	This is used extensively in scripting to display messages for the user. It can also be a useful tool for viewing environment variables by preceding the environment variable with $. Here's an example: `echo $PATH`

Table 6-2: Useful Linux commands.

Command	Function	Usage Notes and examples
apt	Package manager	apt is most commonly used to install new software. It is a more friendly version of apt-get and includes progress reporting. Normal usage: `sudo apt install myprogram`
apt-get	Package manager	apt is now more commonly used.
apt-cache search	Search the Pi repository for software	This will search the Pi repository list for matches to your search criteria. For best results, update the cache first with: sudo apt update. You can use wild-cards in the search, ie apt-cache search fldigi*. This will search for all software containing fldigi.
apt-cache show	Provides details of software in the cache	Use this to get more details of software that you've located with apt-cache search.
grep	A text search tool	This command provides a very powerful text search that can be used on files or the console output. In its most basic form you could search myfile.txt for the word test with the following: `grep test myfile.txt` If test is found, grep will print the entire line containing test. Grep supports the use of search patterns including full regular expressions. There is also a selection of options available to control the search. The most useful options are: -i to ignore case, -v to invert the match, -w only show lines where the match is to a whole word, -x only show complete line matches. You can also use command line options to control the output. Here's are some useful options: -c count the number of matches, -L only print the names of files with no matches, -l only print the names of files with matches, -o only prints the matched part of the line, -n output the line number of each match, -a process a binary file as if it was text.
&	Run program in the background	If you run a program or script, from a terminal session, you can end the command line with a single ampersand (&) to run the program or command in the background.
dpkg	Tool to unpackage .deb packages	Whilst most Raspberry Pi software is installed using the apt command, dpkg can be used to install software that's supplied as a .deb file. A typical example is WSJT-X where the Raspbery Pi binary files are supplied in .deb format. In general, apt is the preferred method of installation because it handles the identification and installation of any dependencies. Typical use would be: `sudo dpkg -i myprogram`
sort	Sort a text file	Used without option, sort produces a sorted list of items from a text file on the screen. With the addition of > you can send the sorted list to a new file, eg: `sort file1.txt > file2.txt`
head	Read the first 10 lines of a text file	To change the number of lines displayed add -n followed by a number, eg. `head file1.txt -n3` will display the first 3 lines. You can also use > to send the output to a new file

Table 6-2: Useful Linux commands (continued).

Command	Function	Usage Notes and examples
su	Substitute user, often used to switch to root	Whereas sudo is used on a line-by-line basis to run commands with administrator permissions, su gives the current terminal session administrator permissions. Whilst the default is to switch to administrator, you can use it switch to any user by following su with the user name.
mount & umount	Mount a device	Use to mount and unmount devices such as external disks.
Tail	Display the last few lines of a text file	Similar to head but displays the end of a text file.

ping	Send a request to a network node	A useful command for checking accessibility of a URL or IP address. Usage is ping followed by the address, like so:
		`ping g4wnc.com`
		`ping 82.71.204.29`
		Ping will continue sending packets and reporting the response times. To stop ping, enter ctrl-C

Ifconfig	Displays the network configuration	A useful check of the connection status of the Pi networking. Use: Ifconfig wlan0 for the first Wi-Fi adapter.
ps	Displays a list of running processes	Without any options, it will only display processes for the user of the terminal session. To see all running processes, use ps -A. To search for a running process, use with the pipe (|) and grep. For example, to find the spyserver process enter: ps -A | grep spyserver
top	Displays a graphical view of running processes	Provides a detailed view of running processes. You can also install htop (sudo apt install htop) for a more sophisticated version of top.
chmod	Modify permissions of a file or directory	This is most commonly used to make a file executable for which the command is: `sudo chmod +x filename`
sudo	Temporary administrator rights	Linux security prevents ordinary users from installing software, changing important system settings or working on files outside their home directory. However, you can temporarily give yourself elevated authority by using sudo ahead of the command or action you want to apply.
kill	Used to kill a running process	Simply enter kill followed by the process ID number. This can be found using ps,top or htop
systemctl	Used to control services (known as Units)	Can be used to start, stop, enable, disable and check the status of any service running on the Pi. The format is: sudo systemctl status myservice.service To see all services use: `systemctl -a` To exit the screen listing, press q
wget	Download files from the web	A very useful utility from downloading files from a url. It is very robust and will keep trying until the file(s) is successfully downloaded. Usage: `wget http://wwwmysite.com/myfile.zip`
git	Download files from the GIT code repository	git is similar to wget but downloads a complete repository and handles the file format used for git code repositories. Typical usage is: `git clone https://github.com/myprograms/myfile.git`

Raspberry Pi Explained

Command	Function	Usage Notes and examples
`tar`	Create extract or maintain files in tar format	This is a tool used to manipulate archives stored in the .tar format. For Pi users, it is most commonly used to unpack archives that are supplied as .tar archives known as a tarball. The most common usage is: `tar -xvzf myfile.tar.gz` The -options do the following: x means extract file, v means verbose so you will see what's going on, z tells tar to use gzip and f tells tar that the filename follows so must always be the last item in the options list.
`7z`	Powerful unzip utility	This needs to be installed: `sudo apt install p7zip-full`
`man`	Display the manual entry for a command	This command provides access to the detailed instructions for any command. To see the manual page for ls, simply enter: `man ls` To exit the manual page press q
`pwd`	Displays the current working directory	A very useful command for checking your place in the filesystem.
`reboot`	Reboots the system	This reboots the system. On most Linux distributions, this requires root permissions. However, Pi Raspbian allows any user to issue this command
`shutdown`	Starts a scheduled shutdown	Shutdown without any options will shutdown the Pi with a delay of 2 minutes and issue a warning message to all the logged-on users.
`poweroff`	Turns the power off	This command immediately shuts off the power.
`hostname`	List or set the Pi hostname	This is the best command for finding the Pi IP address. The usage is: `hostname -I`
`chmod`	Modify permissions of a file or directory	This is most commonly used to make a file executable for which the command is: `sudo chmod +x filename`
`sudo`	Temporary administrator rights	Linux security prevents ordinary users from installing software, changing important system settings or working on files outside their home directory. However, you can temporarily give yourself elevated authority by using sudo ahead of the command or action you want to apply.
`kill`	Used to kill a running process	Simply enter kill followed by the process ID number. This can be found using ps,top or htop
`systemctl`	Used to control services (known as Units)	Can be used to start, stop, enable, disable and check the status of any service running on the Pi. The format is: sudo systemctl status myservice.service To see all services use: `systemctl -a` To exit the screen listing, press q
`uptime`	Displays the time the system has been running	Provides a useful summary of the Pi activity since the last powerup and includes the processor loading and number of users. You can use -p and -s options for a simplified output. Usage is: `uptime`
`find`	Use to find files	To find myfile in the current directory use: `find -name myfile`

Command	Function	Usage Notes and examples
watch	Runs a command repeatedly in the console	Useful if you want to check for changes. For example, watch ls -l could be used to monitor files being transferred into a directory. The default frequency is 2 seconds but this can be changed with the -n suffix followed by the number of seconds. -n 3 would be every 3 seconds
\	Use to extend command-line entries over more than one line	Occasionally, you will need to enter a long string of commands at the command prompt. The \ can be used to continue typing on the next line and helps readability. When you hit Return the shell will ignore the \ and treat the entries as a single line.
&&	Used to combine commands	When joined with && the second command will only be executed if the first command is successful, eg sudo apt update && sudo apt upgrade
||	Used to combine commands	When joined with || the second command will only be executed if the first command fails.
;	Used to combine commands	When joined with ; the second command will always be executed regardless of the success or failure of the first command.

Adding programs to the top task bar

Once you've been using the Pi for a while, a useful timesaver can be to add your most commonly used applications to the task bar at the top of the screen. There are several ways to do this but here is the simplest technique I've found:

1. Right-click on a blank area of the menu bar and select Add/Remove Panel Items
2. Select the Panel Applets tab and click Add
3. Scroll to the Application Launcher Bar, select it and click Add
4. You should now see a + icon to the right of the menu bar
5. You can now use the Up/Down controls to position the +icon on the Menu bar. The top of the list being the far left of the screen.
6. Click Close when the + icon is in the desired position
7. You should still have the + icon on the menu bar
8. Click on the +icon and a navigation panel will appear
9. Navigate to the desired application and double-click. The + icon should be replaced by the icon of your application.
10. At this point, you can add other programs to the Menu bar using the same technique, ie navigate to the program and double-click.
11. When you've finished adding programs, click Close.

As you can see, this is very easy to do and lets you load you favourite programs with a single mouse-click.

Screen shots

The ability to capture screen shots can be very useful when troubleshooting or seeking help from support forums. Raspbian doesn't support the common Windows Print-Screen hotkey for screen captures but there are a few simple tools that I suggest you use.

For many screen shots, the integrated command line tool, scrot, provides a very simple solution. Scrot has several command line options, I've shown a selection of the most common below:

```
scrot -d 5
```

The -d 5 causes scrot to wait for 5 seconds before taking the screen shot. This gives you time to clear unwanted items from the screen.

```
scrot test.png
```

By adding a filename at the end of the command, scrot will save the screen shot with that file name. Without the filename, it will create its own filename based on a timestamp.

```
scrot -u -d 5
```

The -u option takes a screen shot of just the window that's in focus. I normally use this with the -d delay option so that I have time to select the desired window before the screen shot is taken.

```
scrot -s -d 5
```

Like the -u option, the -s option allows you to either click on the desired window or draw a rectangle with the mouse to define the capture area. The -d delay doesn't start until you either select a window or complete drawing the rectangle.

```
scrot -c -d 5
```

The -c option adds a countdown in the terminal window and is used with the -d option.

Here are a few examples that put the commands together.

```
scrot -d 5 -s screen.png
```

Take a screenshot of the selected window after 5 seconds and names the file screen.png

```
scrot -d 5 -s -c screen.png
```

The same as the last example but adds a countdown.

I hope you can see, that scrot is a quick and easy screen grabber that provides most of the features you're likely to need.

Recording screen movies

There are times when it's useful to be able to make a recording of a section of the Pi screen. This could be to help with troubleshooting a problem or to create a tutorial. There are several software packages available, but I use Vokoscreen because it's so quick and easy and does all I need. Vokoscreen is simple to install and has a straightforward interface that makes operation obvious, **Figure 6-3**. Vokoscreen is available from the Pi repository and the following two commands will install the latest version:

```
sudo update

sudo apt install -y voko-
screen
```

Once installed, Vokoscreen can be found via the Pi menu under Sound & Vision. In addition to recording the entire screen, a window, or a mouse drawn rectangle, Vokoscreen can also record from a webcam. Using this option, you can have the webcam image and audio recorded alongside the screen recording. This is particularly good for creating tutorials.

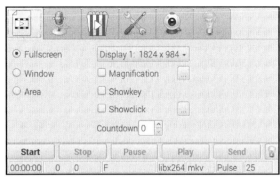

Figure 6-3: Vokoscreen movie capture.

Running software at startup

There will be occasions when you want a program to start automatically when the Pi boots. A good example would be the SDR servers for Airspy and RTL-SDR receivers. These servers provide remote access to Airspy receivers or RTL-SDR dongles over the network and need to be able to run unattended. The default installation of these servers requires that they be manually started after the Pi is up and running. However, it would be so much better if the servers automatically started as part of the boot process. This is particularly important for dealing with power outages as the server would fire-up automatically as soon as the power is restored and the Pi reboots.

How to automate

A common, but unsophisticated, way to auto-start any program, is to use the rc.local file. This script file is automatically executed during boot process so you can add simple Bash commands to start your programs. You can access the file for editing using the nano editor as follows:

```
sudo nano /etc/rc.local
```

Here is the Bash text that we would need to add to the rc.local file to start an RTL-SDR server: /usr/local/bin/rtl_tcp -a 192.168.1.88

An important point here is to make sure you give the full path to the program you want to launch. However, there are a couple of problems with this line. The first is that it will hold a Bash session open. This is easily fixed by adding an ampersand (&) at the end of the line. This tells Linux to run the program in the background. The more serious problem is not knowing the IP address, or even whether the network exists when the Pi starts! In earlier versions of Raspbian, the rc.local file was executed at the end of the boot cycle and usually after the network was active. However, that changed a few releases ago and rc.local is often called before the network is fully available. This is always the case when using Wi-Fi connections, which tend to be slower to setup. If we run the RTL-SDR server command before the network is up, the command will fail, and the server won't start. We therefore need a better solution. Getting the IP address is easy because the default code in rc.local collects the IP address using the hostname -I command and stores it in a variable called $_IP. We can therefore modify our command line as follows:

```
/usr/local/bin/rtl_tcp -a $_IP &
```

This line will run the server in the background using the allocated IP address. However, we still have a problem if rc.local executes before the network is ready. A crude solution would be to force rc.local to pause for a set time before running the server command. We can do this using the sleep command. The following line will add a 10 second delay. Make sure you enter the new line near the beginning of the rc.local file and certainly before the 'hostname' command.

```
sleep 10
```

You can experiment to find a delay that works reliably for your network. A more sophisticated solution would involve some additional code to repeatedly check for the network and then run the server as soon as it's detected. Here's an example script to do just that:

```
counter=1
until [[ \$_IP ]] ; do
  _IP=\$(hostname -I)
  sleep 1
  echo "\`date -u\`:Waiting for IP address - seconds:"
  ((counter++))
  if [ \$counter -gt 30 ]
  then
      echo "\`date -u\` :Network not available, script closing"
exit
  fi
done
/usr/local/bin/rtl_tcp -a $_IP &
```

This script causes rc.local execution to loop until an IP address has been allocated. You will see that I've added a 1 second delay in the loop (sleep 1) and set a limit of 30 on the counter. This causes the script to loop once per second until the network is detected. If no network is found after 30 seconds, the script exits with an error and doesn't try to start the server. I've used this script for a few years to automatically start the RTL-SDR server on the microSD cards that I sell.

SYSTEMD - a better way

As you can see from the rc.local example, the scripting solutions can get quite complex when you want to customise the start-up. Fortunately, there's a better way to manage auto-starting programs that run in the background. This management system is called Systemd and the programs under its control are referred to as Units. For our purposes, the programs that we run under Systemd will be run as services, much like the services you may be familiar with in a Windows environment. Systemd is far more flexible than the rc.local approach, because you have greater control over how these services operate and when they start. For example, you can start and stop services at any time with the following commands:

```
sudo systemctl start myprogram.service
```

```
sudo systemctl stop myprogram.service
```

You can also use a short-cut with Systemd and drop the .service at the end of the command, ie

```
sudo systemctl stop myprogram
```

I've shown a summary of some of the more popular systemctl commands in **Table 6-3** To be able to run our application as a service under Systemd, we first need to create a Unit file that gives Systemd some information about how we want the program to run. That file needs to be stored in: /etc/systemd/system. I'll continue with the example of running the RTL-SDR server as a service. Here's

`start`	Starts an application
`stop`	Stops an application
`restart`	restarts an application
`reload`	Can be used for applications that are able to reload their configuration without stopping
`reload-or-re-start`	Systemd will take the appropriate action for the application specified
`enable`	The enables the application to be automatically started during boot
`disable`	This prevents the application from starting at boot
`status`	This will display the status of the application
`is-active`	Check if the application is running
`is-enabled`	This will report whether the application is enabled for starting at boot
`is-failed`	This will report if the application has failed
`list-units`	This will display all active units (applications)
`list-units --all`	Similar to above but will show all applications that it has attempted to load.

Table 6-3: Systemctl commands.

the unit file I currently use to run the RTL-SDR server:

```
[Unit]
Description=RTL-SDR Server
Wants=network-online.target
After=network-online.target

[Service]
ExecStart=/bin/sh -c '/usr/local/bin/rtl_tcp -a $(hostname -I)'
WorkingDirectory=/home/pi
StandardOutput=inherit
StandardError=inherit
Restart=always
User=pi

[Install]
WantedBy=multi-user.target
```

The first section titled 'Unit' provides a description of the service and the 'Wants' and 'After' entry is set so that this service starts after the network has been acquired. Moving on to the 'Service' section, this describes the behaviour of our service. The 'ExecStart' line is where you put the command line that will run your application. As you can see, this needs to show the absolute path to your executable. This example uses a rather neat trick that calls our program and passes the IP address of the Pi, so let's look at that in a bit more detail.

You might reasonably expect to start the rtl-sdr server with /usr/bin/rtl_tcp -a $IP, where $_IP is the IP address of the Pi. However, when we run rtl-sdr as a service, we don't have a convenient variable available that will give us the IP address. The solution is to start the rtl-sdr server as if we typed it on a command line. When we enter instructions on a command line they are interpreted by Bash. By starting the server as if it was being entered from a command line we can create our own variable to hold the IP address. So, how do we enter a set of instructions to Bash from inside a service? It turns out to be very simple. Instead of running the server, we start by running sh (sh being an abbreviation for Bash) with: /bin/sh. To let sh know that we want it to read instructions from a string, we need to use the -c option and enclose our instruction list in single quotes. Here's the complete ExecStart line:

```
ExecStart=/bin/sh -c '/usr/local/bin/rtl_tcp -a $(hostname
```

```
-I)'
```

In this example, $(hostname -I) creates a variable with the Pi IP address that's passed to the server.

The ExecStart entry is followed by the WorkingDirectory and I've set this to the standard Pi home directory. The next two lines are used to direct standard output and error messages. In both cases, leaving them set at inherit means the output will follow your current settings, which is normally to the screen. The Restart entry specifies what happens to the service if it stops. In the case of our SDR server, we want it to restart. In the final, [Install], section, the single line ensures that the rest of the Linux system is running.

I hope you can see that, running applications such as SDR servers as a service, is a much better way and offers far more control. The ability to start/ stop and check the status of these services can be very helpful if you want to write a simple script to update the server software. I use this in my Spy Server microSD card. As the Spy Server is an evolving project, I wanted a simple way for users to update the software. The solution was a script to check, download and install the latest software. As I have the server running as a service, I can stop the server from inside the script, update the service and then restart the server when finished. This avoids the need to reboot the Pi after the update and the entire process is executed with a simple double-click of a desktop icon!

Running a program after the desktop has started

Another, very simple, way to automatically start a program at boot is to use the PIXEL desktop. The desktop includes an auto-start file where you can set any number of programs to start after the desktop. The autostart file can be found in: /etc/xdg/lxsession/LXDE-pi/autostart. To add a program to the autostart, follow these steps:

Open a terminal session (Ctl-Alt-T) and enter the following to open the autostart file:

```
sudo nano /etc/xdg/lxsession/LXDE-pi/autostart
```

Create a new line above the @xscreensaver line. On the new line, enter the command to start your program. NB: This is the same as the command you use to manually start the program. You should also specify the full path to the program.

Press Ctl-X followed by Y then Enter to close and save the file.

Restart the Pi and your program should run automatically. If your program doesn't run, the most common cause is mistakes in the 'run' line. To test the line, use step 1 to open the autostart file. Copy the 'run' line to the clipboard and paste it into a terminal session to see if it works.

Headless Pi

Whilst the Pi works very well when connected to a keyboard, mouse and monitor, there are plenty of occasions when you will want to use the Pi without all that hardware connected. A good example would be the SDR servers I've already mentioned, but there are lots of automation roles for the Pi that would have the same requirement. Because Linux is used as the core language for many commercial embedded computer systems, it's no surprise to find that the Pi is well equipped for remote or headless operation. The requirement here is for a secure connection method to access the Pi. That is provided using SSH (Secure SHell), which is a well-established cryptographic network protocol that's included in Raspbian. SSH is turned off by default for security reasons, so the first task is to activate it. Here are the steps using the PIXEL desktop:

1. Open the Pi menu and choose Preferences - Raspberry Pi Configuration.
2. Click the Interfaces tab and set the SSH radio button to Enabled.
3. Click OK to finish.

Enable SSH from the command line:

SSH can be enabled from the command line using the raspi-config utility. Here's a step-by-step guide:

1. Open a terminal session (Ctl-Alt-T)
2. Enter: sudo raspi-config
3. Step down to option 5 - Interfacing Options and press Enter
4. Step down to Option P2 - SSH and press Enter
5. On the next screen, select Yes to enable the SSH server and press Enter
6. You will see a splash screen to confirm that the SSH server has been enabled.
7. Click OK and use the tab key to select Finish and press Enter.

At this point, the Pi is ready for headless operation and we can move to another computer on the network to test it out. Before you go any further, the Pi must have a network connection before we can make use of the SSH link, so you will need the IP address. This is easily obtained either by entering: hostname -I at the command prompt or by hovering your mouse over the up/down arrow, network icon on the top bar of the PIXEL desktop.

Install a terminal emulator - Windows PC

To access the Pi from another computer, you may need to install terminal emulator software. There are lots of free versions available and PuTTY is a good starting point for Windows PCs. This is available from: www.putty.org

Once you have PuTTY installed, use these steps to connect to your Pi:

1. Start PuTTY and set the Connection type to SSH, **Figure 6-4**.

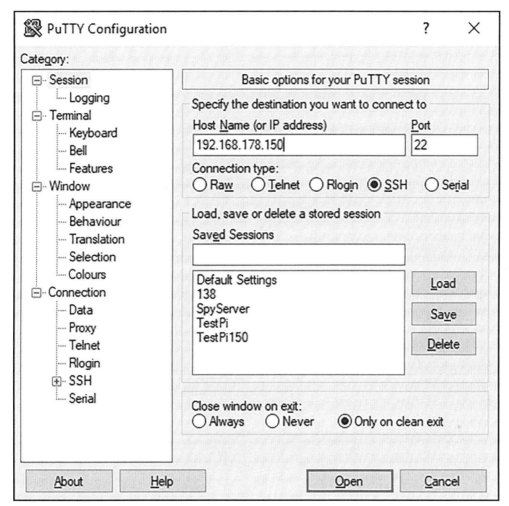
Figure 6-4: PuTTY setup screen.

2. In the Host Name (or IP address) box, enter the IP address of your Pi
3. Click Open at the bottom of the panel to open the connection
4. You will probably get a PuTTY security alert the first time you make the connection, you can answer Yes to this
5. If all is well, you will see a login prompt where you can enter your username (default pi) followed by your password (default raspberry).
6. That will be followed by a copyright and a security warning splash (if you're still using the default password)

You should now be at the Pi command line where you can enter commands as if you were using a keyboard directly connected to the Pi.

SSH connection using a Mac

Using Mac to access the Pi via SSH is simple using the following steps:

Press Command-space to open Spotlight and type Terminal to open the terminal emulator

Enter ping followed by your Pi IP address to check that the Pi is reachable, ie ping 123.123.123.999

1. Connect to the Pi by entering: ssh and the Pi IP, ie ssh 123.123.123.999
2. Enter the Pi username and password to access the Pi command line

You will now see the Pi command line and you can enter commands as if you were directly connected to the Pi.

SSH connection from a Linux PC

The commands used here are virtually the same as with a Mac but the Linux and Mac operating systems are not related, despite what some may claim. There is no need to install a terminal emulator because the default terminal has all we need. Here's the step-by-step guide for setting-up an SSH connection using Linux:

1. Open a terminal session (Ctl-Alt-T)
2. Enter ping followed by the IP address of the Pi to check that it's visible on the network, ie ping 123.123.123.999
3. Press Ctl-C to stop the ping
4. Connect to the Pi by entering ssh followed by the Pi IP address, ie ssh 123.123.123.999
5. Enter the Pi password when prompted
6. You may see a warning regarding the security certificate, but you can answer yes to this.

Once you receive the licensing splash screen, you can start entering commands.

Setting-up a remote desktop connection (VNC)

Whilst SSH is useful for sending commands and moving files, there are plenty of occasions where you may want to access the full Pi desktop. This type of remote connection is known as Virtual Network Computing (VNC). To make this easy, the Pi team have partnered with RealVNC so their VNC server is included in the standard Raspbian distribution. In addition to providing the server and client software free of charge, you can sign-up for a free RealVNC cloud account so you can access your Pi from anywhere there's an Internet connection. The free cloud account sign-up can be found at: www.realvnc.com/raspberrypi/#sign-up

NB: If you only want to connect to the Pi via your local network, you don't need to setup a RealVNC cloud account.

By default, the VNC service is disabled on the Pi, so the first step is to enable

RealVNC using Pi configuration utility as follows:
1. From the Pi menu choose Preferences - Raspberry Pi configuration
2. Next select the Interfaces tab
3. Click the VNC Enabled button to activate the service.

The Pi is now ready to accept connections from a VNC viewer. On the computer you want to control the Pi from, you need to install the VNC viewer software and I suggest you use the free RealVNC viewer (www.realvnc.com). This is available for all operating systems, including mobile devices.

Once installed, connecting to your Pi over the local network is just a case of entering the Pi IP address into the address bar of the RealVNC viewer. Here's a step-by-step guide:
1. Enter the Pi IP address into the address bar at the top of the RealVNC viewer screen.
2. The first time you connect you will see a message that the VNC Server is not recognised. You can click Continue and the Pi server details will be saved
3. The Authentication box enter the Pi username and password. You can tick the remember password box to speed future connections

You should now see the Pi desktop and be able to use it as if you were directly connected.

In **Figure 6-5** I've shown a screenshot of a Pi being controlled using a Windows PC and RealVNC.

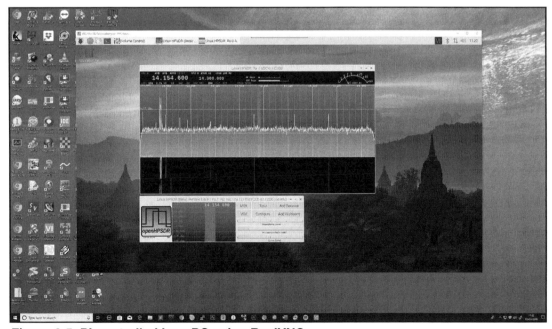

Figure 6-5: Pi controlled by a PC using RealVNC.

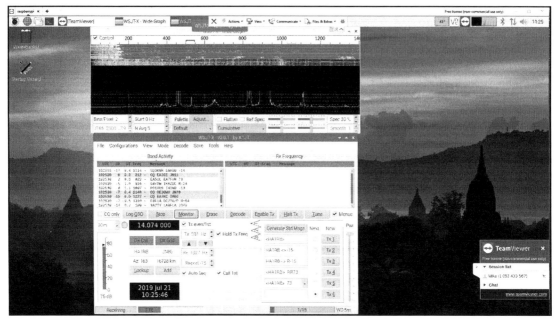

Figure 6-6: TeamViewer running on a Pi.

Remote access with TeamViewer

If you're looking for alternative VNC software then TeamViewer is a good choice. I've been using TeamViewer to remotely manage and maintain my family's computers for many years, and it's proved to be very reliable. By creating a free account with TeamViewer, you can access any other device running TeamViewer via the Internet. Security is managed with a simple user ID and password combination. All you need to access another computer are those two parameters. One of the benefits of TeamViewer is that you can have full Internet remote access without having to enable port-forwarding on your router.

Installing TeamViewer:
A Pi version of TeamViewer, **Figure 6-6**, is available from the downloads page of the TeamViewer site at: https://www.teamviewer.com/en/download/linux/#downloadAdditionalDownloads

When you get to the site, look for the Debian, Ubuntu, Raspbian entry for TeamViewer Host and select the armv7_32bit download link (or simply click on "Download Host) in the separate section entitled "Your start into IoT: TeamViewer Host for Raspberry Pi". This will download a .deb package to the Downloads folder on the Pi. However, before we can install TeamViewer, we need to install some prerequisites. To do that, open a terminal session and enter the commands that follow: NB: This needs to be processed as a single line, but I've added the \ character so I can break the entry over several lines. This helps make the code more readable and reduces the risk of typos.

```
sudo apt install -y qml-module-qtgraphicaleffects \

qml-module-qtquick-privatewidgets libqt5webkit5 qml-mod-
ule-qtquick2 \

qml-module-qtquick-controls qml-module-qtquick-dialogs \

qml-module-qtquick-window2 qml-module-qtquick-layouts
```

When this installation completes, you can finish installing TeamViewer as follows:

Open a terminal session open (Ctl-Alt-T)

Change to the Downloads directory by entering: cd ~/Downloads

Install the .deb package with:

sudo dpkg -i teamviewer-host_15.0.8397_armhf.deb NB: You must change the deb file name to match the version you downloaded.

That completes the installation, so you can find TeamViewer via the Pi menu - Internet. At this point your Pi is not yet accessible so you need to configure TeamViewer by clicking the cogs icon in TeamViewer. On the General screen you can change the display name of your Pi to make it more relevant to its use. In the Network settings you want to accept incoming LAN connections. It is also well worth setting up a free TeamViewer account on their website as it gives you very easy access to the Pi from anywhere with Internet. Once you have your account follow this guide to make the Pi available via TeamViewer:

Start TeamViewer on the Pi and choose Grant easy access. Enter your TeamViewer username and password and click the Assign button.

The TeamViewer site will send an email to your main email address so you can confirm that you want to add the Pi as a trusted device.

Follow the instructions in the email to add the Pi. Once complete, the display on the Pi will change to show your ID number.

That completes the installation and you should be able to open the TeamViewer application on your main PC, sign-in to your TeamViewer account and you will see the Pi listed as one of your partners. To access the Pi and use the desktop, just double-click on the name. In addition to providing full access to the desktop, TeamViewer includes lots of useful tools for file transfer, making recordings or sending key combinations. These are all accessed via the menu at the top of the TeamViewer panel.

File transfers between Windows and the Pi

I've encountered many situations when I've wanted to transfer files between a Windows PC and the Pi. The best way to do this is to use a file transfer client. This is a Windows application that manages the connection between the two systems and provides a side-by-side view of the selected directory in each computer. You can then move files between the two computers using drag and drop. In addition to the basic file transfer, most clients will remember the username/password so the link is very quick to establish. The two (free) clients I recommend are FileZilla (filezilla-project.org) and WinSCP (winscp. net). To set up a connection using FileZilla or WinSCP you will need to know the local IP address of the target Pi. (If you don't already know its address, open a terminal session and enter: hostname -I).

Pi Hardware Quirks

In this chapter I'll introduce you to some of the compromises or design quirks of the Raspberry Pi and show you how to work with them. Whilst the Pi is undoubtedly a design masterpiece, it was built with a challenging price-point in mind so there are a few design compromises that we need to be aware of. These decisions were critical to the overall success of the project and were not taken lightly. The design team's success is clear from the Pi sales figures and the fact that there have been no real competitors at the same price point. Whilst there are many similar Single Board Computers (SBC) on the market that offer faster processors or faster connections, the penalty is usually a higher price along with increased power consumption and cooling problems.

As you might expect from a system as popular as the Pi, its shortcomings are well documented and matched with a variety of innovative solutions. In this chapter I'll focus on how to deal with a few of the design compromises.

Working with audio

The Pi was originally designed to work with an HDMI monitor for both the sound and video output. As a result, it doesn't have a separate, on-board, soundcard, in fact, there are no audio input facilities at all. However, there is a stereo audio output that's available via the 3.5mm jack. The audio output does not use a conventional sound card chip but makes use of a Pulse Width Modulation (PWM) line from the processor that is passed via a low pass filter to provide the audio out. The PWM line is effectively used as a simple digital to analogue converter (DAC). This employs a similar principle to that used for Class D audio amplifiers. The audio quality available from this output was quite poor in the early Pi models. This was due to power supply noise breaking through to the audio. However, the latest models

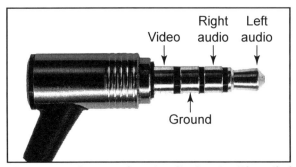

Figure 7-1: Connection details for the Pi audio/ video jack.

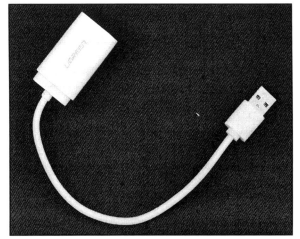

Figure 7-2: The popular U-Green USB audio adapter work well with the Pi.

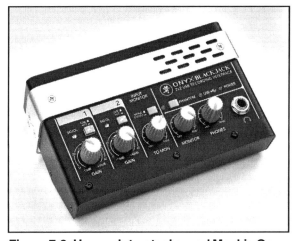

Figure 7-3: Heavy-duty, steel cased Mackie Onyx Blackjack USB sound interface.

include a new buffer chip between the PWM line and the low-pass filter. This provides a useful quality improvement along with a welcome output boost. At about the same time, the wiring of the 3.5mm jack changed and it now carries the composite video signal as well as stereo audio. The wiring configuration is similar, but not the same, as many mobile phones and is shown in **Figure 7-1**.

Adding USB audio

If you need an audio input for your Pi, the simplest solution is to add a USB soundcard. These are readily available from Internet suppliers for around £10. A popular and well tested model is the U-Green USB Audio Adapter, **Figure 7-2**. Whilst the basic USB sound card works fine with radio applications, it can be helpful to have more control of the input and output levels. This can be handled with on-screen controls, but many operators prefer mechanical, rotary, controls as they can be quicker to access. Whilst there are some good custom-designed audio interfaces for radio kit, competition in the home music studio market has created some very good units at attractive prices. Behringer is a popular choice and their UMC22 has separate input and output controls and costs around the £35 mark. A unit that I've used here for some time is the Makie Onyx Blackjack USB sound interface, **Figure 7-3**. This model is particularly good for radio use because it is housed in a heavy-duty steel case and all the input and output jacks are located on the rear panel. That model is no longer in production, and the replacement is the Makie Onyx Artist 1.2 USB that sells for around £90. This still uses a heavy-duty steel case but can handle higher bit-rates than its predecessor. The only downside is the shift of the input and output jacks to the front panel. An alternative solution, is to build your own interface. You will find many designs on the web some of which are very sophisticated. However, you can cover the basics by combining the circuit in **Figure 7-4** with a basic USB sound card like the U-Green mentioned earlier. To keep any stray RF under control you should mount the interface in a screened enclosure. Once you have your sound card hardware, the next step is to get to grips with the way audio is managed in Linux.

Several modern Amateur Radio transceivers have a USB interface to audio and serial communications electronics inside the transceiver. For these only a standard USB cable with the correct connectors is required as long as the chips used in the rig are supported under Raspbian Linux.

Linux audio

The first thing to note is that audio with the Raspberry Pi, and Linux in general, is not quite as straightforward as with Windows. When using Windows, audio devices are automatically recognised and integrated into the system and work with very little direction from the user. Whilst Linux does automatically recognise and install the required kernel drivers, the rest of the configuration sometimes need a little help. This is not necessarily bad news, because the Linux audio system comes with more user control and the ability to route audio to several devices or applications.

The routing control is particularly useful for radio applications as we can transfer digital audio between several applications without incurring the losses associated with analogue looping via a soundcard. In Windows, this routing would be handled by a separate Virtual Audio Cable (VAC) application, but it's built-in to most Linux distributions and is easy (and free) to add if not already installed (use of this feature is covered in chapter 5 - SDR on the Pi).

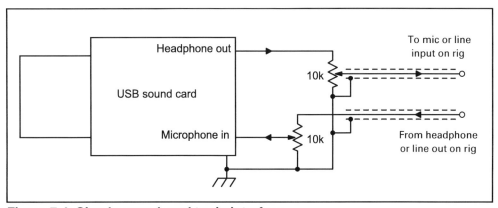

Figure 7-4: Simple sound card to rig interface.

Linux sound architecture

Advanced Linux Sound Architecture, known as ALSA, is the low-level software framework that resides in the Linux kernel and manages the communication with your sound hardware. ALSA provides all the device drivers and has an Application Programming Interface (API) that allows 3rd party software to communicate with the audio hardware. The standard Raspbian Buster operating system for the Pi also uses the BlueALSA audio package to help with routing Bluetooth audio but no longer includes the popular PulseAudio sound server. PulseAudio is a particularly useful audio server as it aids the distribution of digital audio feeds to and from different applications and hardware. It even provides some sample-rate conversion and adjustable latency (delay).

Sound servers

A sound server is an application that sits above ALSA and is designed to provide easier access the Linux sound system. The two most popular sound servers are PulseAudio and Jack. Of these, PulseAudio is the most widespread and is supplied ready installed on many Linux distributions (but not the current Raspbian). PulseAudio is primarily designed to be used for desktop computers and so is optimised for general media and web playback. Jack, on the other hand, has been designed with the music professional in mind and so has extensive facilities to handle sample-rate conversion, multiple routing and latency adjustment. An important point to note here is that PulseAudio and Jack don't always work well together, so it's best to choose one or the other. For amateur radio applications, I have found that PulseAudio is the more useful option.

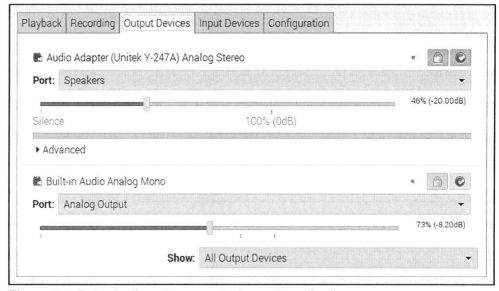

Figure 7-5: PulseAudio volume control panel application.

Installing PulseAudio on the Pi is straightforward and requires the following steps:
Open a terminal session (Ctl-Alt-T)

1. Update the APT repository index with: apt update
2. Next, install PulseAudio with: sudo apt install -y pulseaudio

When complete, test the installation by checking the version by typing: pulseaudio --version

I also recommend installing the PulseAudio Volume Control application. This provides a GUI (Graphis User Interface) for PulseAudio with sliders for level control along with level meters. The control also makes software audio streams visible, thus simplifying the control of signal levels to avoid overload. To install the PulseAudio Volume Control type this command:

```
sudo apt install -y pavucontrol
```

When the installation completes, you will find the volume control via the Pi menu in the Sound & Video section. I've shown a screenshot of the PulseAudio Volume Control in **Figure 7-5**.

Sound oddities

The standard Raspbian installation automatically loads all the drivers for the Broadcom HDMI sound system. This means that the device list will show two Broadcom audio devices, the first of which has six sub devices. These sub-devices are the various surround-sound channels. When using USB soundcards, we don't normally want the HDMI audio devices, but they can cause confusion and certainly clog-up the devices list in applications. I've also seen some applications throw errors because they're not expecting to encounter surround-sound devices. If you're not planning to use HDMI audio, the best solution is to stop the HDMI sound kernel modules from loading at boot. This turns out to be very easy and only requires a change to one line of the Raspberry Pi config file.

Here's a step-by-step guide:
Open a terminal session (Ctl-Alt-T)

1. List the installed sound devices by entering: aplay -l
2. You should see Broadcom sound devices listed
3. Edit the config.txt file using nano by entering:

```
sudo nano /boot/config.txt
```

4. Scroll through the file to find the line (usually at the end):

```
dtparam=audio=on
```

5. Edit this line to read: dtparam=audio=off
6. Close and save the file by pressing Ctl-X followed by Y
7. Restart the Pi by entering: reboot
8. Check for sound devices again by entering: aplay -l
9. The Broadcom devices should have disappeared. If not, double-check your editing

Although the Linux sound system has a huge range of advanced features, it is not the friendliest to use. The situation is further confused by the varied ways software developers can interact with the audio. I've had examples where one program deals directly with the audio at ALSA level whilst a companion application expects to route audio using PulseAudio. If you want to pass audio between these two applications, you can very quickly lose your way! I have dealt with this issue in depth in my chapter on installing radio applications, so jump to that section if you want to know more about passing audio between applications.

USB/Ethernet bottleneck

The BCM2835 processor at the heart of the Pi-3 and earlier models features a single USB2.0 port that was originally designed for use as an On the Go (OTG) port for mobile devices. On the model A and Zero boards, the BCM2835's single USB is wired directly to the single USB socket. This single socket can handle a maximum throughput of 480Mbs, ie the normal maximum for a USB 2 port. However, on the Model B boards, the same BCM2835 port is wired to a combined Ethernet and USB hub chip. This provides the 100Mbase-T Ethernet port and the 2 or 4 USB ports, depending on the model. These ports can handle most modern USB devices but the 480Mbs bandwidth is shared between the requirements of the Ethernet port and the USB ports. There is also a management overhead that will consume some of the available bandwidth. The net result is that the Pi USB/Ethernet hub can be a bottleneck if you are working both the Ethernet and USB ports hard with lots of data. In the Pi-3B+ the situation has been improved by changing to the Microchip LAN7515 chip for the Gigabit Ethernet and a USB 2 hub. However, that chip still relies on the same USB 2 connection from the processor. The net result is a useful increase in Ethernet speed, providing the USB ports are idle. In my experience, Ethernet data rates of up to 300Mb/s can be achieved with the new setup, which is three times faster than the previous 100Base-T port. For full speed Gigabit and USB ports, the Pi-4B is the answer because it uses a different architecture and the Gigabit, USB 2 and USB 3 ports can be operated at full speed. This is a major step forward and resolves the previous data bottleneck.

Pi USB power

I've covered powering the Pi in a separate chapter, but I'll briefly cover the USB power issues here because the early models had some restrictions. A feature common to all the Pi models except the Pi-4B, is their use of a micro USB socket for the DC power feed. This socket is adequately rated for the job and can handle up to 5 amps. However, the early Pi models had polyfuses fitted both in the incoming supply and the feed to each USB port. The USB polyfuse rating was 140mA, thus restricting the maximum safe current draw from each

USB port to about 100mA. This was plenty to drive a mouse or keyboard but well short of the requirements for an external hard drive. Whilst these polyfuses did provide useful, resettable, protection, they could take days to reset, so the user might well assume their Pi has been damaged! This restriction applied to the original Pi-A, B and A+ models. With the introduction of the Pi-2 and B+ models, software switchable USB current limiting was introduced. With this system, the default total USB current was set at 600mA, but could be increased to 1.2A by editing the /boot/config.txt file and appending the line: max-usb_current=1.For the Pi-3B and B+ models, the standard USB current rating was increased to 1.2A. The Pi-4B, Pi-3B+ Pi-3A+, Zero and Zero-W/WH have no limitations on the current draw from their single USB port, other than the capabilities of the PSU, PCB track ratings and the micro USB connector.

Pi serial ports

The introduction of Bluetooth on the Pi-3 and Pi-Zero-W brought some changes to the way serial ports are handled on the Pi. This was necessary because Bluetooth is a serial connection protocol that requires a serial connection into the Broadcom SoC at the heart of the Raspberry Pi.

For all models except the Pi-4, the Pi SoC features two serial ports, one of which is a full featured hardware UART (Universal Asynchronous Receiver Transmitter) whilst the other is a software defined UART (mini-UART) with limited functionality. Before the Pi-3, whenever we wanted to make use of the Pi serial port, it was accessed using the device name: /dev/AMA0, which is the standard name for an ARM based UART port. As that port is now used for the Bluetooth chip in some Pi models, the Pi team created a new alias or nickname for the serial ports to simplify access. Instead of referring to serial ports directly as /dev/AMA0 or /dev/ttyS0 you should now use the more logical alias of /dev/serial0 and /dev/serial1. The mapping of these aliases to the UART ports will depend on the model Pi you are using and the options are set in the file: /boot/config.txt. The Pi team recommend always using serial0 for serial port access using GPIO pins 14 and 15. In practice, that means that serial0 will point to the mini-UART for models with Bluetooth active and the hardware UART for all other models. This ensures that you will always have a serial port mapped to GPIO pins 14 and 15. If you have a wireless model and don't need the Bluetooth facility, you can easily reconfigure the Pi to release both serial ports as I'll show you here.

Using mini-UART

For many applications, the mini-UART is adequate, but we need to make a change to the configuration to activate it. One of the weak points of the mini-UART has been its dependency on the system clock for its baud rate. This is problematic because the Pi system clock can change depending on the operating mode. The original solution was to add the line: core_freq=250 to the /boot/config.txt file. However, that has changed recently and in the latest Raspbian, you simply add enable_uart=1 to the /boot/config.txt file to activate the mini-UART and fix the system clock problem.

Accessing the hardware UART on a Pi-3 and earlier

If you have a Pi expansion board that mounts on the GPIO pins and requires the hardware UART on pins 14/15 there are two options available. If you don't require the Bluetooth capabilities of the Pi-3, you can simply disable the Bluetooth service, which will automatically free-up the hardware UART serial port and reconnect it to pins 14 and 15. To disable the UART add the following line to /boot/config.txt:

```
dtoverlay=pi3-disable-bt
```

You also need to disable the hciuart service by entering the following:

```
sudo systemctl disable hciuart
```

Now restart the Pi and you will find that both serial devices (/dev/serial0 and serial1) are available and serial0 will be connected to the hardware UART.

Swapping UARTs

If you want access to the hardware UART via the standard GPIO pins but also continue with Bluetooth functionality, you will need to swap the hardware and software UARTs in the Broadcom chip. This is a simple task because the Broadcom chip is a SoC (System on a Chip) device with software configurable pin mapping. Changing pin allocations is done using Device Tree overlays in the /boot/config.txt file. The success of the swap will depend on how hard you intend to use Bluetooth. This is because the mini-UART is slower than the hardware UART and has limited flow control. To implement the swap, you need to add a couple of lines to the /boot/config.txt file. The first line remaps the Bluetooth to the mini-UART and connects the hardware UART back on GPIO pins 14 and 15. Access the file for editing with:

```
sudo nano /boot/config.txt
```

Then add this line at the end:

```
dtoverlay=pi3-miniuart-bt
```

Next, we need to fix the core clock frequency. This is required because the mini-UART baud rate is linked to the core frequency and this can change when the Pi goes into power saving mode. Here's the line you should add to the end of the config.txt file to fix the core frequency:

```
core_freq=250
```

That completes the swap and you should have full access to the hardware

UART via /dev/serial0 or /dev/AMA0 using the standard GPIO 14 and 15 pins.

Pi-4 serial ports

The Pi-4 with its updated SoC, now includes 4 additional hardware UART ports. This means that we can move away from the rather cumbersome arrangement which we had with earlier Pi models where we had to swap-out the Bluetooth UART to get access to a hardware UART. Before we can use the new ports, they must be enabled in the /boot/config.txt file. The new UARTs are numbered 2 to 5 and when activated will be available via /dev/ttyAMA1 to ttyAMA4. To activate the first additional UART add the following line to the [pi4] section of /boot/config.txt as shown here:

1. Open a terminal session and open the /boot/config.txt file by entering:

```
sudo nano /boot/config.txt
```

2. Scroll down the file that opens until you reach the [pi4] section
3. In that section add a new line that reads:

```
dtoverlay=uart2
```

4. To close and save the file enter Ctl+X followed by Y.

If your application requires use of the CTS/RTS flow-control lines you can activate them by adding the following additional line to the /boot.config.txt file.

```
dtoverlay=uart2,ctsrts
```

The new UART ports are made available via the GPIO pins and to see the pin allocation use this in-built tool from the command line:

```
dtoverlay -h uart2
```

You can also use the following command to see all possible GPIO pin allocations.

```
raspi-gpio funcs
```

Useful serial port commands

Here are a few Linux commands that can be entered in a terminal session to show how the serial ports are configured:

```
ls -l /dev | grep serial
```

This will show you which hardware ports are assigned to serial0 and serial1.
ls /dev/ser*

This will list the active serial ports.

```
cat /dev/serial0
```

This will direct the incoming serial0 data to the screen.

Summary

In this chapter I've looked at a few of the Pi design compromises and showed how they can be mitigated. There is no doubt that the Pi-4 solves the long-standing limitations of the Pi platform and, if only for that reason, is the model to go for.

Programming the Pi

Computer programming for practical people

I have a slightly different approach to programming than most that has been born out of the need to get things done and I'll share that here. I'm very much a part-time programmer and my bouts of activity are usually triggered by a project that requires a software solution. Because I only program occasionally, many of the skills and techniques I use to solve a problem quickly evaporate as I move on to other things. That leads to wasted time when I next need to do some programming. My personal solution involves a couple of actions. The first is to add plenty of comments in my code to explain what what's going-on and how it works. As well as providing a useful reminder, the comments are very helpful if I want to change the code at a later stage. I also keep copies of all my code in one location on the PC so it's easy to find and backup. The second action is to write down a few notes about the techniques I learnt whilst creating a project. These act as a very useful refresher for next time.

What I can't do here is teach you to be a good programmer in a few pages. However, I might just be able to set you off the right path.

When you decide to try your hand at computer programming, the first challenge is to decide what language to use. There are just so many out there, ranging from the well-established C and C++ to Python, JavaScript, Nodejs, HTML5/CSS and some of the newer languages such as GO from Google. Your choice should be based on what you're trying to achieve and how you like to work. If you want to have very close control of the hardware and have dabbled with Arduinos, then you are already part way down the route to learning C and C++, so that may be your best route. If you want to program at a higher level with a simpler, more readable language, then Python is a great choice. Python is also one of today's fastest growing programming languages. If, on the other hand, your interest centres on web services, then you really need to be heading for JavaScript, Nodejs, HTML and CSS. However, many of you may not want to specialise at this time but just need an easy-to-use, general purpose language that can do a bit of everything. In that case, I recommend you head straight for Python. In addition to being easy to learn, Python is very well supported with lots of free tutorials and ready-made code. Python also has many free and lively support forums that are happy to give you advice on programming problems. For those reasons, most of the coding examples in this book use Python.

Programming introduction

One of the underlying principles of good programming practice, regardless of the language, is to avoid writing the same code more than once. The thinking here is that, if you've spent time writing and debugging code, it should be pre-served in some way so that next time you need to do the same task, you can reuse your original code. Not only does this save time but it minimises the risk of introducing new bugs into your software. Another important principle is to keep it clear and simple. Once you've written your code and it's working properly, you should re-examine it to see if it can be further simplified/clarified. The idea here is to make the code more efficient and easier to reuse.

Program development

Before you get stuck-in to learning and writing code, you need to analyse and clearly note what you're trying to achieve. One popular technique is to use pseu-docode. This might sound complicated but pseudocode is just a plain language, detailed list of the things that you want the program to do. You can make-up your own words to describe the actions, but the act of writing it down, forces you to think carefully and logically about what you're trying to do and how you might achieve it. Once you've documented the program in pseudo-code, coding the project becomes very much easier. If you don't think the program through be-fore you start coding, you'll end-up writing unnecessary code and very quickly get in a pickle! If you don't like the ideal of using pseudo-code, at least draw a detailed flow chart of how the program will work.

Pseudo-code example

Let me illustrate the pseudo-code technique with a simple example of a program that will toggle an LED on and off every time a button is pressed. The first code we need must check whether the button has been pressed. This is a simple task but we're going to repeatedly check the button, so how can we do that without having to retype the code? The solution is to put the button checking code into what's called a function and give it a unique name. In this case, we could call it button_check. The name I've chosen uses a formatting style commonly used in Python that replaces inter-word spaces with an underscore. This gives easy-to-read names for functions and variables whilst avoiding spaces and other characters that can be troublesome or simply not allowed in some programming languages. In addition to checking whether the button has been pressed, our button_check function needs a way to let us know when the button's been pressed. We can do this by making the button_check function send a signal back to the main program. This is known as the return value and, in this case, we'll assume button_press returns 1 if the button is pressed and 0 if not. The other task we need to do repeatedly, is to toggle the state of the LED. By toggle I mean turn it on if it was previously off and vice-versa. It would make sense to use the same technique and create a new function called toggle_led.

Now our simple program has two functions: button_check and toggle_led. Although, the main activity is captured by those two functions, we need some extra code or glue to link the functions and make a working program. The first requirement is a decision to control whether or not to toggle the LED. A simple technique, that you'll find in most programming languages, is the IF command. This takes the form: IF X Then do Y or ELSE do Z. Let's now list the program steps we've created to see how it looks:

```
Start

IF button_check = 1

THEN do toggle_led

Or ELSE do nothing
```

That gives us the basic functionality we need as it will check the button and toggle the LED, but it will only run once and stop, which is not a lot of use. Ideally, we want it to keep checking the button. We could do that by looping back to the beginning. However, a simple loop would keep repeating the code at the maximum speed the processor could handle. That could be millions of times a second and we probably don't want to do that! A simple way to control the frequency of button checking is to add a delay to pause the program each time it loops. Here's a rewrite of the program with the delay added:

```
Start

IF button_check = 1

THEN do toggle_led

Or ELSE do nothing

delay 0.1s

Return to Start
```

This program will now loop continuously checking for a button press about 10 times per second. That should be enough to catch all the button presses. At this point, you might think you're ready to start coding but, this simple program already has a bug. Can you spot it? What happens if, with the LED off, we press the button and release it slowly? A slow release could easily keep the button contacts closed for 2/10ths of a second, which is long enough for the program to loop round twice and report two button operations. Instead of just changing state as expected, the LED will just flicker (on for 1/10th second then off again). For a longer button press, the final state of the LED would depend on whether the button was pressed for an odd or even number of 1/10ths of a second. This is a long way from the clear toggle action we were hoping for. One simple, but crude, fix would be to add another delay after a button press has been detected. This would suspend the normal checking for a pre-set time to allow the button to be released. Here's the program again with the extra 1 second delay added:

```
Start

IF button_check = 1

THEN do toggle_led delay 1s

Or ELSE do nothing

delay 0.1s

Return to Start
```

Whilst this fix may be good enough for this application, it remains a crude solution and has given our button a very sluggish response. This is because we will have to wait at least 1 second between button presses or they will be ignored. This solution is leading us down a slippery slope that will result in a bad program. This is because we've started adding code to the main program to deal with shortcomings in the workings of the button_check function. The real solution here is to specify exactly how we want the button_press function to perform. It's only when you start to think deeply about the program that you realise exactly what's required from the different elements. From our analysis, we want the button_press function to only return a pressed value (1) to the main program when the button has been pressed and released. With that behaviour, the LED will always toggle once for both short and long button operations. For the pseudo-code example, let's assume the button is connected to GPIO pin 1 on the Pi and wired to be low when the button is pressed and high when open. Here's the pseudo-code for button_press:

```
Function: button_press

IF GPIO pin1 = high

THEN return 0 (not pressed)

ELSE keep checking GPIO pin 1 till it goes high, then re-
turn 1
```

I hope you can see that this is a much better solution, because the function will only return the value 1 at the end of the button press, regardless of the duration of the button press. The button will now feel very responsive and we can confidently start writing the code.

This simple example illustrates the importance of thinking carefully about how you want your program to behave under different scenarios.

Code libraries

This brings us nicely on to code libraries. Once we've spent time designing and writing the code for detecting the button press, it would make sense to keep it somewhere safe so we could reuse it in other projects. That would be a great timesaver as we could use the code with confidence knowing the bugs have been ironed-out. We could do the same for the toggle_LED function and maybe save both functions in the same file and make it the start of our own code library. Code libraries are such a good idea that they are used by all modern programming languages and have revolutionised computer programming.

If we think back to our button_press function, there's an opportunity to make it more useful in other projects by adding some additional code. The function as planned will only work with a button connected to pin 1 of the Pi GPIO. However, it would be infinitely more useful if we could use the code to deal with a button connected to any GPIO pin. To do that, we would have to tell the function which GPIO pin to monitor. That's easily done as all program languages include a way to send information to a function. If we go back to our pseudo-code it could look like this:

```
Function: button_press (A)

IF GPIO pin A = high

THEN return 0 #(not pressed)

ELSE # keep checking GPIO pin A until it goes high, then
return 1
```

In this example, the pin number is sent to the function in a variable called A. From this you can see that we could send any pin number we like to the function. In a practical solution we would probably need some additional coding to make sure the range of acceptable pin numbers matched those available in the Pi. When we start increasing the usefulness of a function it often gains additional internal functions and maybe even its own data. In those cases, the code would normally be converted into a different type of container called a class.

Introducing Python

Let's start with a quick example to show how code libraries are used in Python. Let's go back to our original LED and button program and see how we could do that on a Raspberry Pi using Python 3. Because reacting to buttons and controlling LEDs is an everyday task, the Pi has a special code library called gpiozero preinstalled. This has classes available to do the two tasks in our program. The two classes we need are called Button and LED, and we can import them into our program with this single line:

```
from gpiozero import Button, LED
```

All the code in the gpiozero library is thoroughly tested and highly versatile, which gives us the flexibility to connect our LED and button to any of the available Pi GPIO ports. Of course, we need to tell the classes which pins we're using, and we do that like so:

```
button = Button(20)

led = LED(21)
```

This creates two new objects where the first is called 'button' (note the use of lower-case) and is connected to pin 20 whilst the new object 'led' is connected to pin 21. These new objects inherit all the features of the library code but are now assigned to those specific names and pins. For the rest of the program, we can use just the object names 'button' and 'led'. However, if we wanted to have two buttons, the second button would need a different, unique name, eg 'button2'. Our two new objects, called 'led' and 'button' come with several methods that we can utilise. For example, 'led' has a built-in method called 'toggle'. This method automatically toggles the state of the LED, so we don't have to write that code. The button object also has a method called 'wait_for_press' so we don't need to write code for that either. Our complete LED toggle program in Python looks like this:

```
#!/usr/bin/env python3

from gpiozero import Button, LED

button = Button(20)

led = LED(21)

while True:

button.wait_for_press()

led.toggle()
```

In this example, the line: while True: is a common Python trick for making a program repeat continuously. This is not good practice for production software but can be very useful for testing short code blocks such as this. One important point to note is the use of indents. These are important in Python and are used to separate code blocks. For that reason, the lines after while True: are indented so they form part of the 'while True' code-block and will be executed inside that loop.

At this point, you may be wondering what's the purpose of the odd looking first line that begins #! This is called a shebang and is used in Unix and Linux systems to allow a text file to be treated as an executable file. Without this, a Python script has to be run by entering: python myprog.py. With a shebang in the first line, you can drop python. However, you would still need to give the Python script permission to execute using: sudo chmod +x myprog.py.

Python, like most of the popular programming languages has a huge range of software libraries available, many of which are already installed on the Pi. As you will see in the later chapter on interfacing, add-on board suppliers for the Pi, usually have matching code libraries available for free download. This helps make Python and the Pi an ideal combination for developing applications that interact with the home, workshop, radios, etc.

Learning Python

I'm not going to attempt to teach you Python, but I can help you with some useful resources to set you in the right direction. There are currently two versions of Python in common use and they are version 2.7 and 3.x. I suggest that those new to Python learn version 3 as that is the improved version that will have long term support. At the moment, version 2.7 is still very useful and some code libraries are only available in 2.7 flavour. However, a gradual changeover to version 3.x is in progress and 2.7 will eventually wither away.

One of the essential tools for both learning and writing any programming language is an Integrated Development Environment or IDE. This might sound intimidating, but an IDE is just a combination of a text editor with whatever programming language you're using. It's perfectly possible to write good software using the simplest of text editors, but an IDE is a big help for newcomers and can speed program development. In addition to providing the text editor, the IDE is usually linked to the programming language so you can run and test your code from inside the IDE. The language link also provides automated syntax checking and code formatting to add indents and the like. The better IDE's also let you run through your program one step at a time, which is great for tracking down problems. The standard Raspbian operating system includes IDEs for all the popular programming languages and I suggest you use either Thonny or Geany for Python. Thonny is a dedicated, Python only, IDE and is very simple to use, whilst Geany supports many different programming languages including Python. In **Figure 8-1**, I've shown a cropped screen shot of Thonny with

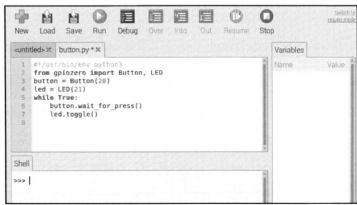

Figure 8-1: Geany general purpose programming IDE.

the button-press program displayed. In this example, the indents and text high-lighting were added automatically by Thonny.

Python learning resources

A search of the Internet for Python tutorials will return many pages of hits, so it might be helpful if I provide some guidance. My preferred way to learn is through doing, and to that end, learnpython.org has a wonderful and free tutorial available for Python 3. This provides a simple tutorial that guides you through all the key points of the language. What makes this tutorial particularly attractive is its use of interactive code panels, **Figure 8-2**. Here you can type and execute code in the left panel and see the results immediately displayed on the right. It's a very powerful learning tool that gives you the freedom to experiment and check your understanding of each topic, whilst inside the tutorial. Books for learning Python are plentiful but I suggest you read the reviews carefully to find a book that suits your level of knowledge and learning preferences. The Raspberry Pi maga-zine MagPi has produced several books including the excellent Learning Python with the Raspberry Pi. The MagPi magazine has also covered programming very well and there are a couple issues that are of particular interest to new programmers. The first is in issue 53 where they published a Beginner's Guide to Programming and the second is in Issue 54, Understanding Object Ori-entated Programming. All MagPi issues are free to download as PDF files.

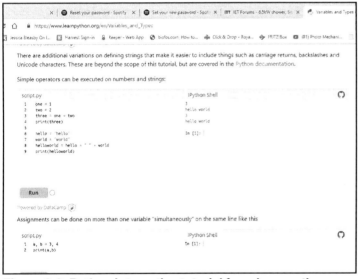

Figure 8-2: Python interactive tutorial from learnpython.org.

Writing shell scripts

When you get familiar with Linux and the Pi, there will be many occasions when you need to run a series of instructions on the command line. A typical example could be to update a program that is only available as source code. In that case, you would have to manually enter the build instructions and wait for each stage to complete before you could enter the next instruction. This is where a shell script can save time. A shell script is no more than a list of commands that are stored in a text file and can be automatically executed. All the standard commands are available, but you can add some refinements to keeps you informed of progress and provide error messages if things go wrong. Here's an example of a basic script that will update and reboot your Pi.

```
#!/bin/sh

sudo apt -y update

sudo apt -y upgrade

reboot
```

This starts with the shebang for a shell script followed by the same commands you would enter at the command line prompt. However, this script doesn't give us any progress reports or tell us where things went wrong in case of failure. Progress reports can be added by printing text back to the screen at each stage of the script. The command for this is echo and the text we want displayed should be enclosed in quotes (single or double). To display 'Program Complete' we could use the following:

```
echo "Program Complete"
```

You can try this from the command line, but you must leave a space between the command echo and the quotes. Using this technique, we can easily add progress reports before and after each section in the script. If the script were to fail, it would be helpful to see a meaningful error report. This is easy to do using the double-pipe command ||. This acts as a switch where the code following the double-pipe is only executed if the code prior to the double-pipe fails. Like so:

If this fails || execute this

Here's an example but with a real command:

```
sudo apt -y update || echo "Update failed"
```

This will result in 'Update Failed' being printed in the terminal should the update command fail. Although this provides a useful progress report, it won't necessarily stop the script, so we need to add a bit more. To force an exit from a shell script, we can use the command exit but we ought to give it a numerical value to indicate that it was caused by an error. As a normal, error-free, exit from a script returns 0, we'll use 1 as our exit code. The exit code can be added to the existing line using a semicolon, like this:

```
sudo apt -y update || echo "Update failed"; exit 1
```

When creating a longer script, it's good practice to clearly separate the error messages from the main code. One common method is to put the error code on a separate, indented, line, enclosed in curly braces like so:

```
sudo apt -y update ||

{echo "Update failed"; exit 1 }
```

Here's an example of the complete, update, upgrade and reboot script with progress and error reporting:

```
#!/bin/sh
```

```
echo " Starting update… "
sudo apt -y update ||
   {echo "Update failed"; exit 1 }
echo "Starting upgrade…"
sudo apt -y upgrade ||
   {echo "Upgrade failed"; exit 1 }
Echo "Restarting your Pi …"
Sleep 5
Restart ||
   {echo "Restart failed"; exit 1 }
```

NB: You will need to give this file permission to execute with sudo chmod +x myprog.sh. Once that's done, you can execute the script with: ./myprog.sh

The scripting style I've used here is not the most common, but it does make the script relatively easy to read for a novice. If you want to make serious use of scripts, I suggest you look at the Google Bash Style Guide as this provides very comprehensive guidance for all aspects of Shell scripting. You can find the guide here: https://google.github.io/styleguide/shell.xml.

Shell scripts are probably one of the easiest programming tools to work with and can be great time savers. They also help you fully exploit the powerful Linux command line tools. I use scripting extensively to build my specialised Pi SD cards and they save me so much time. The shell script can also be used as a useful store for complex command sequences that you might only use occasionally.

Amateur radio programming

Given that there are code libraries available for most of the complicated stuff, creating a useful application is all about combining code libraries and hardware to perform the desired task. I tend to think of programming in much the same way as a home brew project. We rarely make our own components instead, we buy ready-made resistors, capacitors, transistors and chips. We also use development boards to provide the building blocks for larger projects. However, we still need to make those vital interconnections to create the desired functionality. When it comes to writing software, we can use the same strategy and take advantage of code libraries for most of the functionality, just adding our own code to link it all together for our project.

Visual Programming: One aspect of computer programming that's seen rapid growth in recent years is the use of visual programming. By that I mean applications where the required functions are drawn using flow charts or other visual aids and the software then generates the supporting code in the background.

Scratch:

Scratch is a good example of a visual programming language and has been included in the standard Pi Raspbian for some time. It was developed by the Massachusetts Institute of Technology (MIT) to encourage young people to create their own, interactive, stories using computer programming. I've shown a screen shot in **Figure 8-3**. Scratch programs are constructed by slotting together interlocking blocks. These blocks contain all the normal programming controls but in a friendlier format. This gives students the freedom to concentrate on the program structure instead of having to worry about the idiosyncrasies of coding syntax. Scratch has proven very successful and is now used extensively in schools. Although Scratch is optimised for creating stories, it now includes Pi GPIO connectivity so it can also be used to build small programs that interact with the General Purpose Input Output (GPIO) pins.

Node-RED:

Node-RED describes itself as a graphical event wiring tool. This means that it responds to incoming events, eg button-press, web request, sensor signal, etc. These events can then be combined and processed to generate other events. For example, if a temperature sensor reported a reading below a set threshold, Node-RED could trigger an output that would turn-on the boiler. For the radio amateur, Node-RED could read callsigns being sent from a DX Cluster site and trigger a text message or tweet when a wanted callsign is detected. Whilst Node-RED was originally devised to support communications between Internet of Things (IoT) devices, it is capable of much more. Node-RED can be particularly useful in amateur radio because it provides a simple way to linking all manner of dissimilar devices or software with the minimum of programming expertise.

Node-RED Background:

Node-RED started life back in 2013 as a side project run by Nick O'Leary and Dave Conway-Jones in the IBM Emerging Technologies division. They were experimenting with ways to handle messages passing between a diverse range of hardware. An example could be a home automation system

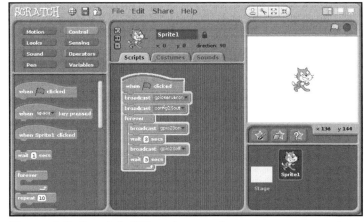

Figure 8-3: Scratch IDE main screen.

where you might to interconnect the boiler, programmer, radiator controls and thermostats. You might also want to add control via the Internet and possibly include control of the lighting, doorbell, etc. The net result is messages being sent at random intervals from an assortment of different hardware, probably with different message formats. For the developer, writing bespoke code to link these interfaces can be very time consuming. This makes the development process both difficult and expensive. Once they'd identified the problem, the Node-RED developers soon realised that the solution could be to write a collection of code blocks to transform the various message types into a common format. Once in the standard format, the messages could be combined and processed at will and the code blocks reused for other projects. The conversion code blocks are called nodes and are be freely shared via the Node-RED repository. The authors could have stopped at that point, but they went a step further and devised an intuitive visual interface for interconnecting and processing these messages. The idea proved to be an immediate success and Node-RED was born. Whenever new hardware is released, the developer only needs to write the code for a new node once and it can then be shared for others to use via the repository.

Node-RED has now gained widespread use and proven to be a great prototyping tool for testing and demonstrating a design before committing to bespoke code. In fact, it's so good that many hobbyists are now using Node-RED to build the final solution.

Node-RED and Raspbian:
Node-RED has been associated with the standard Raspbian OS distribution for some time now and is ideally suited for use with the Pi. In the latest Raspbian Node-RED is not installed in the standard build but is available in the Recommended Software list. To access this and install Node-RED open the Pi menu and select Preferences - Recommended Software - Programming - Node-RED. This will install Node-RED and make it available via the Programming menu. Like all successful programming solutions, Node-RED has a very lively support community and there are currently around 250,000 modules in the Node-RED package repository! These modules cover a huge range of applications and can be freely downloaded and modified.

Installing the Latest Node-RED and Node.js: If you're intending to do some serious programming with Node-RED I recommend you download the latest version of both Node-RED and Node.js. The Node-RED team are aware of the importance of the Raspberry Pi platform so have produced a custom script that will automatically install or upgrade Node-RED and Node.js.

Here's a step-by-step guide:
1. Open a terminal session (Ctl-Alt-T)
2. Enter the following as a single line:
    bash <(curl -sL https://raw.githubusercontent.com/node-red/raspbi-an-deb-package/master/resources/update-nodejs-and-nodered)

3. Hit Enter and the script will download and install the latest versions. This may take a while so let it run its course.

You can also use this script to automatically update both Node-RED and Node.js.

Node-RED on the Pi:

To start Node-RED, go to the Pi Programming menu and select the Node-RED entry. This will open a terminal session where Node-RED will go through its start-up sequence and report that the server is running at http://127.0.0.1:1880. To access Node-RED, you need to open a web browser on the Pi and type http://127.0.0.1:1880 into the address bar. You can also use the name localhost (localhost:1880) as this will also direct you to Node-RED on the current computer. You can also access Node-RED from a different computer on your local network, if that's more convenient. In that case, you need to enter the IP address and port of your Pi into the address bar of the alternative computer. Here's an example that assumes your Pi has an IP address of 123.321.0.2.

```
http://123.321.0.2:1880
```

Simple Node-RED example

When you first access Node-RED you will see a blank worksheet as shown in **Figure 8-4**. Here you will find a list of all the available nodes in the left-hand panel, an empty flow in the centre and a status panel on the right. Programs in Node-RED are called flows because they take the form of a flow chart. Let's start with a very simple flow to show you how it works.

1. From the list of nodes, select the Inject node from the input section (normally at the top).
2. Click and drag this onto the flow.
3. Go to the output section and drag a Debug node onto the flow. You will see that each of the nodes you've used has a connection point marked with a small square. Connections on the right of a node are outputs and those on the

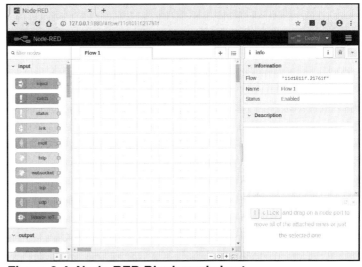

Figure 8-4: Node-RED Blank worksheet.

left are inputs.

4. Click and hold on the inject node output and drag a connecting wire to the debug node input.
5. At this point, you should see a blue dot on each node. That indicates that the node has not yet been deployed.
6. Deploy the new flow by clicking the Deploy button at the top right of the Node-RED screen.
7. You will see a message to say that the flow has been successfully deployed.

At this point we have created a new flow, but we haven't given it any instructions, so the flow is idle. Messages in Node-RED use a standard format known as JSON and the packaged messages are called the payload. Let's now generate a message for our flow:

1. Double-click on the inject node (probably called timestamp) to open the Edit Inject node panel.
2. With edit panel open for the inject node, use the Payload drop-down to set it to timestamp.
3. Move down to the Repeat section, choose Interval.
4. In the box below, set to every 1 second.
5. Click the Deploy button.

We have now set the Inject node to generate a Linux timestamp every second and pass it to the Debug node. If you go to the right-hand panel and select the Debug tab (bug icon) you will see a timestamp message appearing every second. The Debug panel simply reports the output from the debug node. Let's try another change:

1. Double-click on the inject node (now called timestamp) to open the edit panel.
2. Change the Repeat entry to none.
3. Click the deploy button.

Our flow is now idle again, but we can initiate a new message by clicking on the button to the left of the Timestamp inject node. I've started with these two nodes because they are very useful testing nodes for checking the operation of a new flow. The inject node can be set to generate any message and the debug node can take its input from anywhere in the flow. This means you can inject a test message anywhere in your flow and use the debug node to view the message anywhere in your flow. You can also leave multiple debug nodes in your flow and control their output using the button on the right-hand side of the node.

The Linux timestamp in this script is not very useful, so let's see how we can turn it into a more readable format. There are a couple of ways to convert the date. We could use a Function node and write some JavaScript to reformat the date. However, you can be sure that code for date conversion must have been written many times, so there's a good chance someone will have shared their code through the Node-RED website. There are several solutions available but the one we'll use here is called simpletime. Here are the steps to find a new node and install it:

1. In the Node-RED window, click on the three horizontal lines to the right of the Deploy button.
2. Select the Node-RED Pi website.
3. Click Flows on the top menu.
4. In the search box enter: simpletime

This will take you to the entry for the node-red-contrib-simpletime node, where you can read about the node and see the installation instructions. When installing new nodes, it must be done from inside the Node-RED directory. This is a hidden directory called .node-red and it's immediately below the Pi directory. To see the directory with the File Manager, you will have to go to the View menu and tick Show Hidden. Here's the instructions for installing and activating the simpletime node:

1. Open a terminal session (Ctl-Alt-T).
2. Change to the Node-RED directory by entering: cd ~/.node-red
3. To install the new node enter:
   npm install node-red-contrib-simpletime
4. When the install completes, restart Node-RED by entering:
   node-red-restart
5. Open a new browser window and return to Node-RED by entering:
   http://127.0.0.1:1880

In the Node-RED browser window, scroll through the nodes in the left-hand panel and you will see simpletime listed in the Functions section. The simpletime node is very easy to use as it simply monitors the incoming messages and only reacts when it sees a timestamp. All other messages are passed through without change. When a timestamp is detected, simpletime adds extra payloads to the message as described on its website. For example, the date can be found in msg. mydate, whilst the time is in msg.mytime, etc. Let's now add the simpletime node to our flow by connecting it between the inject node and the debug node, **Figure 8-5** (overleaf). Next double-click on the Debug node and use the Output drop-down to

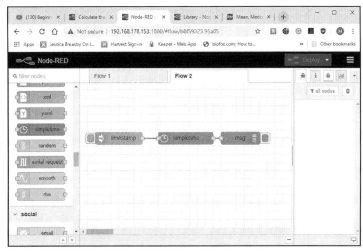

Figure 8-5: Simpletime added to the flow.

set the Output to 'complete msg object'. Click Done to save the changes and Deploy the flow. Now when you press the inject node button, a different message will be displayed in the Debug window. Click on this message to expand it. You should see that the message still has the original timestamp but it also has a long list of extra payloads, that have been generated by the simpletime node. These additional payloads can be extracted and used by other parts of your flow. For example, to see the date in the debug panel, change the Output field in the Debug node to read msg.mydate. NB: You don't need to add the period between msg and mydate as it's already provided. Once the change has been made, click deploy and then click the timestamp button to send a new message. You should find that the date appears in the debug panel.

Summary

This chapter has only scraped the surface of what is possible when you start writing software for your Pi. For the occasional programmer, Python is a very useful language to learn as it is so flexible, and the code is portable between operating systems. Python is also very well supported with plenty of online forums and ready built code libraries. Learning to program can be a very frustrating process as you will hit points where your code fails to do what you want, despite repeated checking. It's at this point that many give up, whereas this is the very time when you learn the most so stick with it. There is always an answer and when you find it, the hard-learnt mistake will be remembered, and you can move on.

Pi Interfacing

Connecting to the outside world

Whilst you can do amazing things with the Pi plus monitor, keyboard and mouse, there will come a time when you want the Pi to interact with the outside world. This could be to read weather data from a sensor, enable CAT control of your rig or simply to switch things on and off. The Pi is very well setup for all these tasks via the on-board GPIO (General Purpose Input Output) connector. In addition to providing lines that can be switched between logic 0 and 1, it can receive 0s and 1s as an input but also supports several common serial data protocols such as SPI (Serial Peripheral Interface) I2C (Inter-Integrated Circuit communications) and traditional UART based serial communications.

Protection required

The inclusion of the original 26-pin and latterly a 40-pin GPIO port is very welcome but comes with a warning. The GPIO pins are directly connected to the processor and limited to 3.3V logic signals! This creates two potential problems. The first is the risk of static damage during handling. This can be offset by good working practices such as making sure you handle the Pi whilst wearing an earthing strap and using anti-static work mats. However, that still leaves the Pi at risk from the second potential problem - the application of a stray 5V logic signal or other unexpected voltages. There are two common protection techniques in use. The first is to buffer the GPIO pins with either a dedicated buffer chip or resistor/ diode voltage clamp, **Figure 9-1**. A more common solution is to use an SPI or I2C

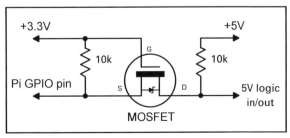

Figure 9-1: GPIO protection circuit.

based bus extender to create new, isolated input and output connections. This need for protection has spawned all manner of expansion boards for the Pi. There's too many for me to cover here, so I'll illustrate the operation with a few of the more popular solutions that I've found useful.

GPIO pin numbering

The numbering of the Raspberry Pi GPIO port has caused a degree of confusion because there are two numbering systems in use, so let me explain why. The Broadcom chip at the heart of the Raspberry Pi, provides GPIO pins that are numbered sequentially. However, some of these pins have a dual role and can be used for serial interfaces such as I2C and SPI. When laying out the original Pi PCB, it made sense to keep these special function pins physically grouped together. The net result is that there is no alignment between the Broadcom GPIO pin numbering and the actual layout on the Raspberry Pi 26-pin or 40-pin connectors. For the sake of clarity this book uses the Broadcom (BCM) GPIO pin numbering. I've shown a drawing of the two pin numbering schemes in **Figure 9-2**.

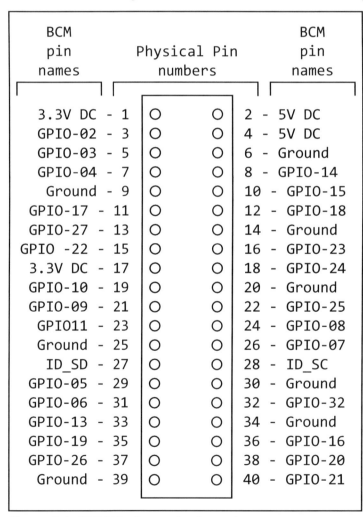

Figure 9-2: Pi GPIO pin numbering schemes.

GPIO Zero

One of the primary goals of the Raspberry Pi Foundation has been to get more students involved in computer science and a vital part of that involvement is getting the Pi to interact with the outside world, also known as physical computing. The simplest interaction is via the GPIO ports on the 26 or 40-pin connector of the Pi. This used to be a bit of a messy process, so the

GPIO Zero Python library was developed to provide a simpler solution. In addition to enabling easy use of GPIO pins, the GPIO Zero library has been regularly updated to include direct reading of many popular sensors as well as supporting SPI and I2C communication protocols for the more advanced add-ons. The GPIO Zero library and all references in this book refer to the BCM numbering scheme. The GPIO Zero library is pre-installed in the standard Raspbian distribution and is intended for use with Python 3, though many of the features may also work under Python 2.x. To import the library into your script just add: import gpiozero near the start of your script. When imported in this way you need to reference items fully using this format:

```
button = gpiozero.Button(20)
```

If you're only intending to use a few functions from GPIO Zero, you can import just those items using this format:

```
from gpiozero import Button
```

Here's a simple example that toggles an LED connected to GPIO 21 when a button connected to GPIO 20 is pressed.

```
from gpiozero import Button, LED

button = Button(20)

led = LED(21)

while True:

button.wait_for_press()

led.toggle()
```

Pi HAT

Just before I move on to some practical solutions, you need to be aware of Pi HATs. The launch of the '+' series of Pi models introduced a new GPIO port configuration with 40 pins in place of the original 26. To retain compatibility with 3rd party add-on boards, the pin allocation of the first 26-pins remained the same. In addition to providing access to extra connections, the new 40-pin GPIO has two pins set aside for communicating with Pi Hardware Attached on Top (HAT). The HAT protocol was developed to make connecting the Pi to the outside world a much simpler process. Before the HAT, users had to interact with the kernel to make sure the appropriate drivers were loaded to support communications for their add-on board. The HAT overcomes this issue by including a small I2C ROM on the HAT that is automatically checked by the Pi during boot and then loads the appropriate drivers. This system has proven very successful and helped to make 3rd party peripherals very easy to use.

GPIO buffering - expansion boards

I've called the following, expansion boards rather than prototyping boards, because they're ready to use as a finished solution. In addition to providing well buffered inputs and outputs, some of these boards conveniently use screw terminal connectors for their external wiring.

PiFace Digital 2:

This is an excellent general-purpose expansion board featuring 8 digital outputs and 8 inputs that are accessed using SPI via the on-board MCP23S17 chip. Each of the 8 outputs has an LED connected making it easy to observe the state of any output pin. In addition, outputs 1 and 2 are connected to a pair of on-board relays via a user selectable link. These relays are rated at 20V 5A, so have a very useful switching capacity. To help with testing, the first 4 inputs have push-switches fitted. Perhaps the best feature is the provision of screw terminal blocks for all the inputs and outputs. I've shown a photo of the board in **Figure 9-3**.

The board is designed to be accessed via the Python PiFace code libraries that are freely available and can be installed as follows:

```
sudo pip3 install pifacedigitalio

sudo pip3 install pifacecommon
```

If you prefer to use Python 2 libraries, use the same commands but change pip3 to pip.

To complete the installation, you need to activate SPI communications using raspi-config. This can be done via the command line with: sudo raspi-config or in the desktop by selecting the Start button and choosing Preferences – Raspberry Pi Configuration. Choose the Interfaces tab and click the radio button for SPI Enabled. If you're intending to use Wi-Fi, you must also use the configuration utility to set the Wi-Fi country or the Wi-Fi will be disabled.

Once the libraries have been installed, using PiFace Digital 2 is very easy. I always find examples are the best way to learn, so I've included a simple example here that will flash the LED on pin 0 and activate the relay once per second.

Figure 9-3: PiFace Digital 2 expansion board for the Pi.

```
import pifacedigitalio as piface

from time import sleep

piface.init()

while True:

piface.digital_write(0,1)
```

```
sleep(1)

piface.digital_write(0,0)

sleep(1)

piface.digital_read(8)
```

To help you understand what's happening, here's the same program with comments added to each line:

```
import pifacedigitalio as piface # Imports the library
with the nickname piface

from time import sleep # Sleep is used to provide the 1
second delay

piface.init()  # Initialises the PiFace SPI chip

while True: # Starts a never-ending loop through the fol-
lowing code

piface.digital_write(0,1)  # Causes pin 0 to go high

sleep(1) # Provides a 1 second delay

piface.digital_write(0,0) # Causes pin 0 to go low

sleep(1) # Provides a 1 second delay

piface.digital_read(8) # Reads the value of pin 8
```

Although this simple program does the job, it ties-up a lot of processor time doing nothing. When writing programs that interact with people, there are many occasions when the software will be waiting for a button to be pressed or something else to happen. To avoid wasting processor time repeatedly checking several input pins, we can make use of interrupts. The name describes the function well because an interrupt will literally interrupt the processor from whatever it's doing to service a new request. In **Figure 9-4** I've shown an example of a Python program that monitors all four buttons on the PiFace board and

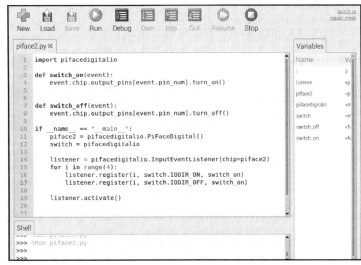

Figure 9-4: PiFace Python program to monitor all buttons and operate the appropriate relay/LED.

operates the relay and selected LED when the respective button is pressed. In this example it's the listener service that monitors for an input and manages the interrupt request. After importing the code libraries, the program creates two functions to turn an output pin on or off respectively. Later in the program you will see the listener entry that monitors the first four input pins and calls the switch_on or switch_off function to activate/deactivate the appropriate output pin and relay. For more information follow the documentation link from the PiFace web page at: www.piface.org.uk.

Pimoroni Automation HAT and pHAT:

Figure 9-5, shows photographs of these two popular expansion boards. These two boards use the Pi 40-pin header to provide easy access to several inputs and outputs as shown here:

- **3** x 24V tolerant digital inputs.
- **3** x 24V tolerant digital outputs that can sink 500mA to ground.
- **3** x 24V tolerant analogue inputs.
- **1** x 3.3V analogue input (HAT only).
- **3** x 24V, 2A changeover relays (just 1 relay on pHAT).
- **15** x channel indicator LEDs (HAT only).

The Automation pHAT is a smaller version of the Automation HAT that has a single relay and no channel LEDs. This board matches the Pi Zero very nicely but can also be used on the full-size Pi. The boards use an ADS1015 4-chan-nel Analogue to Digital Converter (ADC) that links to the Pi using I2C communications. The three analogue inputs that are wired to screw terminals are fitted with a resistive divider network to scale the 24V input range down to 3.3V max. The digital outputs are derived from the GPIO lines and driven by a ULN2003A Darlington array chip. The Darlington array is ground connected, so the outputs act like switches to ground. The digital inputs connect to the GPIO pins but are 24V tolerant and protected by a resistor and 3.3V Zener diode network. The relays are driven from the GPIO pins using the ULN2003A device. I've shown a block diagram in **Figure 9-6**.

Installing the Python libraries is a fully automated process using the instructions available from the Pimoroni GitHub site here: https://github.com/pimoroni/

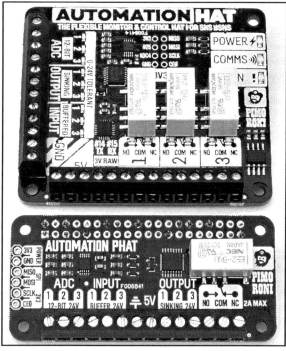

Figure 9-5: The Automation HAT and pHAT.

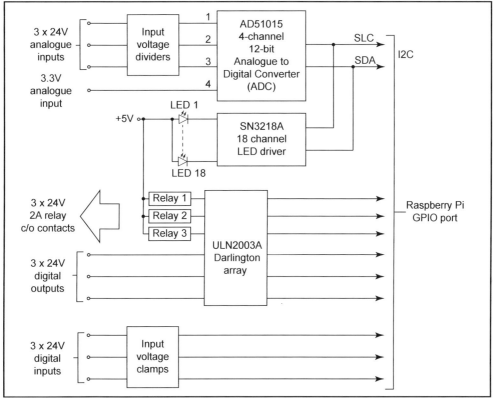

Figure 9-6: Automation HAT simplified block diagram.

automation-hat. The libraries have been designed to make the Automation HAT very easy to use, so let's take a closer look and try a few examples.

Before we can use the Automation Hat libraries in Python, we need to import the library with:

```
import automationhat
```

To read from an analogue input we use:

```
value = automationhat.analog.one.read()
```

As in previous examples, preceding each command with automationhat is a lot of typing, so we can abbreviate this by assigning the library an alias or nickname. To use ahat as the alias we enter:

```
import automationhat as ahat
```

Once we've allocated the alias, the analogue input command becomes just:

```
ahat.analog.one.read()
```

The analogue inputs of the Automation HAT use a 12-bit ADC and give a good accuracy of 2%. If you want to read the value of all the analogue inputs in one line, you can do that with the following command:

```
ahat.analog.read()
```

This returns the measurements from all 4 (3 for pHAT) analogue inputs as a Python dictionary like so:

```
{'four':1.5, 'three': 1.2,'two':4.5, 'one':12.5}
```

To read all the ADC ports and print the value of input 1, use the following:

```
results = ahat.analog.read()

print results.get('one')
```

Prototyping boards

The boards covered here are ideal as learning aids or for helping develop a final project. The key element here is flexibility along with ease of wiring.

Explorer pHAT & Explorer HAT Pro

You can see a photograph of the versatile HAT version in **Figure 9-7**. Both boards are packed with inputs and outputs making them ideal for the experimenter. Here's a run through the features:

- Four buffered 5V tolerant inputs.
- Four powered 5V outputs (can sink up to 500mA total).
- Four capacitive touch pads (labelled 1, 2, 3, 4).
- Four capacitive crocodile clip pads (labelled 5, 6, 7, 8).
- Four coloured LEDs (red, green, blue, and yellow).
- Four analogue inputs.
- Two H-bridge motor drivers (up to 200mA per channel; software PWM control).
- A heap of useful (unprotected) 3v3 goodies from the GPIO.
- A mini breadboard on top.

As the Explorer HAT complies with the Pi HAT standard, the communications ports with the Pi are automatically setup so you don't have to worry about that. Before you can start using the Explorer HAT, you should install the supporting Python libraries. Pimoroni have a script for this so you can open a terminal session and use the following:

```
curl https://get.pimoroni.com/explorerhat | bash
```

In addition to installing the libraries, this command installs full documentation for the Explorer boards along with plenty of examples to help get you started. I'll run through some of the basic utilisation here.

To make use of the Explorer Hat libraries in a Python program, we need to import them with:

```
import explorerhat
```

I like to save some typing effort by using an alias so expand the import command to:

```
import explorerhat as ehat
```

From now on, we can refer to the built-in command by using ehat instead of explorerhat.

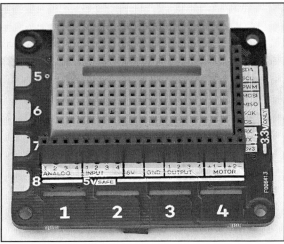

Figure 9-7: Explorer HAT Pro and pHAT.

Motor Control:

The two motor ports are easy to control with the following commands available:

```
ehat.motor.one.forwards()

ehat.motor.one.backwards()

ehat.motor.one.stop()

ehat.motor.one.invert()
```

For the forwards and backwards commands, you can control the motor speed by adding a number in brackets between 1 and 100, eg ehat.motor.one.forward(50), would start the motor at 50%.

You can also start both motors with a single command by omitting the motor number, eg ehat.motor.forwards(50). This will start both motors at 50% and ehat.motor.stop() will stop both motors.

Touch Pads:

These pads provide a useful input facility that is supported with event handlers. Event handlers are a much nicer way to handle user input as you don't have to write loops to continually check for button presses, etc. Here's a very simple Python program that monitors the touch pads and prints-out the channel and the action.

```
import signal

import explorerhat as ehat

def handler(channel, event):

    Print("That was a {} on channel {}".format(event, channel))

ehat.touch.pressed(handler)

ehat.touch.released(handler)

signal.pause()
```

Here's a quick explanation of this program. We're importing 'signal' to give us a clean exit and 'explorerhat' to access the advanced functions that come with the Explorer Hat. The line starting 'def handler …', defines the action to be taken when a touch pad is pressed or released. Let's skip down to the bottom of the program, where the lines ehat.touch.pressed and ehat.touch.released specify the conditions we want to use. In this example, I've set the condition 'pressed' and 'released' to call the function called 'handler'. However, you can also use a different handler for each touchpad action. In this example, the function 'handler' is created in the line beginning 'def handler…' This handler gets the two variables that are returned by the Explorer Hat touch library and prints them to the console output.

Analogue Inputs:

The four analogue inputs are provided by an ADS2015 chip that's connected to the Pi via I2C. All of the inputs have a resistor network included to scale the measurements to a useful range of 0 to 5V DC. The ADS2015 is a 12-bit chip, so the resolution is excellent at 1.22mV and the accuracy should be around 2%. Reading information from the analogue inputs is very simple with the following code:

```
voltage = ehat.analog.one.read()
```

Just replace 'one' with the channel number for the other channels. The library also includes a useful event handler that will automatically call a function when the input voltage changes by more than a specified amount. Here's a simple example that will print the input value if it changes by more than 0.5V.

```
import explorerhat as ehat

import signal

def printVoltage(pin, value):

    print(pin, value)

ehat.analog.one.changed(printVoltage, 0.5)

signal.pause()
```

Digital Inputs:

The digital input pins on the Explorer Hat can be accessed using the standard Raspberry Pi gpiozero library. However, accessing the pins using the Explorerhat library simplifies the code and adds some new features. To read the logic state of pin one use:

```
io = ehat.input.one.read()
```

In this example, the variable io will return a 1 or 0 depending on the state of the input. Another useful addition is the 'has changed' event that returns True if the pin has changed state since the last read. This helps to avoid missing a button press. However, the Explorer Hat library adds event handlers for the digital inputs, so you won't have to keep checking a pin if you're waiting for it to change state. The events available are: on_changed, on_low and on_high. Each of these can be supplemented with a bounce time in ms to help avoid multiple calls from real switches. Here's an example that prints when input 1 goes high but also includes a 0.5 second debounce pause.

```
Import explorerhat as ehat

Import signal

def printState(input):

    data = input.read

name = input.name

print("Input {} is now {}".format(name, data))

ehat.input.one.on_high(printState, 500)

signal.pause
```

Digital outputs and LEDs:

The digital outputs on the Explorer Hat use a ULN2003 chip that provides open-collectors outputs, as shown in **Figure 9-8**. When the Vin pin is set to logic 1, the open collector transistor is turned fully-on, so it acts like a closed switch but when the pin is set to logic 0, the output changes to look like an open switch. This configuration is ideal for switching external devices, pro-

viding you remember that the output pin is completing the ground connection to the supply not the positive rail. The open-collector outputs of the Explorer Hat can switch a maximum of 500mA (that's shared, so if one is switching 300mA the others have only 200mA available). The four Explorer Hat output pins are connected to the Pi GPIO pins 6, 12, 13 and 16, so can also be used with the standard Pi GPIO Zero library However, the Pimoroni Explorer Hat Python library add lots of useful features that I'll briefly cover here.

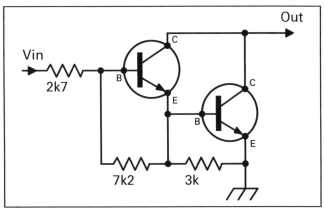

Figure 9-8: Example of the open-collector outputs of the ULN2003.

This is how you turn an output pin on and off:

```
ehat.output.one.on()

ehat.output.one.off()
```

You can also use a numeric representation of the pin number, in which case, they number 0 to 3. Here are the on/off commands again:

```
ehat.output[0].on()
```

```
ehat.output[0].off()
```

It is also possible to send a boolean value (True/1 or False/0) to the output pins like so:

```
ehat.output.one.write(True) or ehat.output.one.write(1)
```

To save having to create a loop to flash an output pin, Explorer Hat has a blink command that's used as follows:

```
ehat.output.one.blink
```

This is supplemented by a more sophisticate pulse command that use Pulse Width Modulation (PWM) to fade the output. The format for the command is:

```
ehat.output.one.pulse(fade-in, fade-out, on-time, off-time)
```

Here's an example to fade-on the output for 2 seconds, fade off for 0.75 seconds, stay on for 1 second and an off time of 0.5 seconds:

```
ehat.output.one.pulse(2, 0.75, 1, 0.5)
```

There is also a convenient single command to stop all fades and blinks as follows:

```
ehat.output.stop()
```

If you just want to stop output on pin one use:

```
 ehat.output.one.stop()
```

In addition to the digital outputs, the Explorer Hat also has a set of four on-board LEDs (yellow, blue, red, green). These can be controlled with all the commands used with the digital outputs and the individual colours are addressed as follows:

```
ehat.light.yellow.one()
```

Enviro pHAT:
I've included this neat board from Pimoroni, **Figure 9-9**, because it is perfect for any project that requires environmental or motion measurements. The Enviro pHAT is the same size as a Pi-Zero so could be combined with a Pi-Zero-W to create a very powerful Wi-Fi connected monitoring node. The board has dedicated sensors for temperature, pressure, light level, light colour, 3-axis motion, compass heading, plus four analogue inputs! These latter inputs can be used to read data from other sensors such as a rain gauge or even a remote SWR meter. The inputs are scaled to read 0 to 3.3V DC by default, so you will probably need to add some resistive voltage dividers to deal with real-world conditions, **Figure 9-10** shows some examples. The

ADC chip employed is the ADS1015, as found in the Explorer Hat. This offers a resolution of 0.8mV with the default settings and the basic accuracy will be about 2%.

Figure 9-9: Enviro pHAT.

The supplied Python library simplifies access to the sensors by automatically converting the raw data to human readable format. Here's a run through the commands used to retrieve data. As in my previous examples, I've imported the Enviro pHAT library this time with the alias wx. Here's the line of code to do that:

Import envirophat as wx

To retrieve details of the light colour and brightness you can use the following commands:

```
colour = wx.light.rgb()

brightness = wx.light.light()

rawValues = wx.light.raw()
```

The colour sensor (TCS3472) can also be used to measure the colour of any object placed immediately in front of it. However, the subject needs to be illuminated, so the Enviro pHAT includes a couple of white LEDs to do just that. These illumination LEDs can be turned on/off as follows:

```
wx.leds.on()

wx.leds.off()
```

The colour sensor can produce very accurate colour measurements, but to realise this, you will need to take a reference reading so you can add a

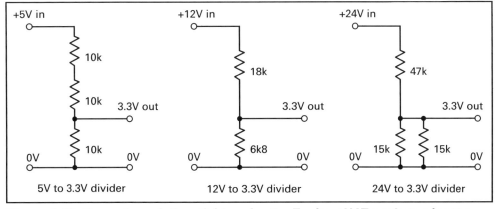

Figure 9-10: Example resistive dividers for the Enviro pHAT analogue inputs.

correction for the colour temperature of the two illuminating LEDs. To take the reference reading you need an item of a known colour value. The cheapest and easiest way to do this is to borrow a photographer's grey card and use it as the reference. If you can't borrow a card, then the grey cardboard rear cover of a notepad is usually a neutral grey. With the grey card in place, take a reading from the colour sensor and compare readings with the true value for the grey card. As the grey card is colour neutral, the readings from all three channels should be the same. I've tried this with my Enviro pHAT and an xRite ColorChecker grey panel, which gave a reading of 79, 96 and 117 (RGB), indicating that the illuminating LEDs have a strong blue cast. The simplest correction is to add/subtract a correction number to the red and blue channels so they all read 96. In this example you would need to add 17, 0 and -21 respectively. If you need accurate colour in your application, the best way to apply it would be to add a Python script that will take the raw reading and automatically apply the correction. Here's a simple Python function to handle the colour correction:

```
def ccolour():

    trueRGB=[]      # Declares trueRGB as a Python list
    cfactor = (17, 0, -21)    # These are the RGB
    correction values

    rawRGB = wx.light.rgb()    # Read the RGB values from
    the sensor

    for x in range(3):          # Iterate over the 3 raw RGB
    values and add the correction

    trueRGB.append(rawRGB[x] + cfactor[x])

    return trueRGB
```

You can use this function to get the correct colour thus:

```
trueColour = ccolour()
```

This will return a Python list with the red, green and blue values.

Pressure and temperature sensing is provided by a BMP280 device that can be read with the following commands:

```
temp = wx.weather.temperature()

pressure = wx.weather.pressure()

altitude = wx.weather.altitude(qnh=101000)
```

NB: The sensors units are Pascals, so you have to divide by 100 to get the more familiar hPa or mb.

The BMP280 automatically updates its sensor when you read a value but you can also force an update with: wx.weather.update()

Analogue Inputs can be accessed in several ways and so offer lots of flexibility. To read the voltages from all four inputs use:

```
wx.analog.read_all()
```

This will deliver the results as a list in a Python tuple (See Python basics). If you want to read a single channel, then the following example for channel 0 will work.wx.analog.read(0)

When using channels numbers, they count from 0 to 3. The Enviro pHAT library includes access to a couple of other ADC parameters that are the gain of the programmable amplifier and the sample-rate. In most cases you won't need to alter those settings but it's useful to have access. Here's an example of reading from analogue channel 0 with the amplifier gain at 512 and a 2.4kHz sample rate:

```
wx.analog.read(0, 512,2400)
```

The positional sensor on the Enviro pHAT board uses an LSM303D device that has 3D accelerometer and 3D magnetometer modules, each of which have three channels of 16-bit data. The 3D raw data from these devices is readily accessible using the following commands:

```
wx.motion.magnetometer()
```

```
wx.motion.accelerometer()
```

Perhaps more useful is the device heading that can be accessed as follows:

```
wx.motion.heading()
```

```
wx.motion.raw_heading()
```

The first command provides a fully tilt compensated heading in degrees, whilst the raw option just provides the magnetometer data.

For such a small and inexpensive device, the Enviro pHAT provides a huge amount of data that could be helpful in a very wide range of projects.

Energenie:
Using the Pi or any other single board computer to control mains voltages can be tricky if you want to stay safe. One excellent solution, that I've used on many occasions, is the wireless switchable mains sockets provided by Energenie UK. A search of any of the online electrical stores will reveal lots of remote switched mains sockets but the Energenie stands apart because of its Raspberry Pi support. The Energenie plugs use the 433MHz ISM band for the radio link between the controller and the socket. In the case of the Pi, Energenie have produced a small remote transmitter board, Pi-Mote that plugs into the GPIO connector of the Raspberry Pi, **Figure 9-11**. This was originally designed for the early Pi boards with 26 GPIO pins, but still works fine on the later 40-pin boards, provided you plug it into the first 26 pins (see also Chapter 3 Pi Projects, for a project using the Pi-Mote board).

Figure 9-11: Pi-Mote controller for Energenie mains plugs.

To compliment the hardware, Energenie also supply a Python library to simplify the programming. This combination has proved so successful that Energenie control has been added to the ZeroGPIO module that is pre-installed since the Stretch release of Raspbian. Using the Energenie board with Python couldn't be easier. In addition to controlling a single socket, the Energenie system can be used to control a group of plugs. The Pi-Mote supports up to 4 groups and each group can have multiple plugs associated thus creating a very flexible switching system. To add a socket to the control group, you press and hold the green button on the plug until the red LED flashes. That indicates that the socket is in 'learn' mode'. If you send an on or off signal from the Pi with the group number you want to use, the socket will receive the signal and the LED will stop flashing. This indicates that the programming is complete. Using the Pi library is easy and here's some examples:

```
from gpiozero import Energenie  # Import the Energenie
part of the library

lamp1 = Energenie(1)  # This initialises an instance of
Energenie for group 1

lamp2 = Energenie(2) # AS before but for group 2

lamp1.on() # Lamp 1 turns on

lamp1.off() # Lamp 1 turns off

lamp2.on() # Lamp 2 on

lamp2.off() # Lamp 2 off
```

Summary

One of the many strengths of the Pi platform is the huge range of 3rd party add-onboards that have been developed as the Pi has evolved. A key factor in this success has been the early standardisation of the GPIO format and pin allocation. This has given suppliers the confidence to invest in the platform and develop these wide-ranging interface boards. In addition to the hardware boards, most suppliers also provide supporting software libraries to make the boards easy to use. In this chapter I've only scraped the surface of what's available. When starting on a new project, it's well worth taking the time to do a few web searches as you may well find that someone else has been working on a similar project and you may be able to adapt some of their ideas.

10

Keeping Time

Many applications, especially the latest amateur radio digital modes, require precise timing to work at their best but the Pi, in its standard form,
can fall short of these requirements. We've already looked at some of the Pi
design compromises but one we've not covered is the lack of a Real-Time
Clock (RTC) to maintain basic time and date information when powered
down or disconnected from the Internet. Given that the primary market for
the Pi was the education sector, omitting the clock was a reasonable decision as the Pi was likely to spend most of its time connected to the Internet,
where accurate time is readily available. However, some applications may
not have an Internet connection available. In those cases, the Pi will start
with a default date and time that's determined by the operating system.
This shortfall is easily fixed using one of the many 3rd party timing options.
The simplest and cheapest solution is to add a plug-in RTC module. These
comprise a very small plug-in PCB, **Figure 10-1**, that contains a dedicated
clock chip and a button cell battery or a supercap (super capacitor). The

latter two items are used to
keep the clock running when
the Pi is powered down. The
technology here is much the
same as your wristwatch.
However, when used in the
Pi, the RTC is synchronised
with the Internet when online and keeps running in
the background when away
from the Internet or when
the Pi is powered down. If
your Pi doesn't connect to

Figure 10-1: Plug-in Real Time Clock modules.

141

Figure 10-2: USB-GPS dongle.

the Internet at all, you can manually set the initial time. The next alternative is a basic GPS solution with a GPS, USB dongle, **Figure 10-2**. In this case, we use the GPS time that's extracted from the positional data received from the GPS satellite. This is sent to the Pi via the USB port. This solution is easy to use and provides an accuracy of about a quarter of a second. Although you might expect better accuracy from a GPS based system, it is the use of serial data over a USB link that limits its accuracy. The ultimate timing solution, which is also the most expensive, is to use a dedicated GPS timing unit that can supply an accurate Pulse Per Second (PPS) output. When using this option, the date and time information is sent to the Pi over a serial connection, but the PPS output marks the precise start of each second. It's the addition of the PPS line that provides micro-second accuracy. Here's a cost comparison of the timing options, based on prices at the time of writing:

RTC Module: £5
USB, GPS Dongle: £12
GPS + PPS board: £35

RTC modules

RTC modules are readily available for the Pi and normally comprise a very small PCB that mounts directly on to the GPIO pins, **Figure 10-3**. Two chips dominate the market, namely the PCF8523 and DS3231. Several experimenters have carried out testing of these two chips and the results show that the DS3231 is significantly more accurate, so I suggest you look for an RTC with that chip. You will also find there's a choice between RTCs using a mercury button cell for back-up power or a supercap. The latter being a very high value capacitor, typically 5 Farads or more. The supercap is charged whilst the Pi is powered-up and is used to keep the clock running when the Pi is powered-down. When com-

Figure 10-3: RTC module mounted on a Pi-4B.

paring the two power options, the supercap offers a much longer lifespan than the battery and is the better option for most applications. However, the battery option is better if the Pi is likely to be powered-down for 6 months or more.

Installing a Real-Time Clock:

With the Pi powered down, mount the RTC board following the supplier's instructions. All the popular RTC modules use the I2C (Inter-Integrated Circuit) serial communications protocol to pass time data to the Pi, so we need to make sure we have the necessary tools and change the configuration to enable it.

Here is a step-by-step guide:

1. Use the Pi menu button and select Preferences - Raspberry Pi Configuration
2. Click the Interfaces tab and enable I2C
3. Click OK to finish
4. Open a terminal session (Ctl-Alt-T)
5. Enter: sudo apt -y install python-smbus i2c-tools
6. You may get a message to say these are already installed, that's fine.

With your RTC board fitted to the Pi, let's now check that I2C is working. Open a terminal session and enter:

```
sudo i2cdetect -y 1
```

If all is well, you should see a matrix printed on the screen with the number 68 printed on the line where 8 and 60 intersect **Figure 10-4**.

The next stage is to alter the Pi configuration file and set it to load the driver

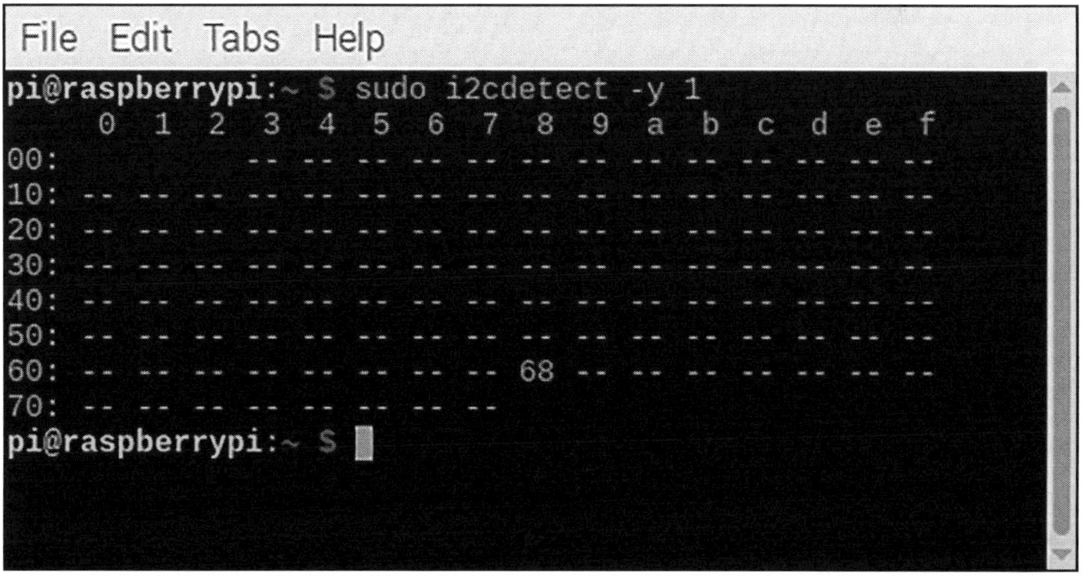

```
File  Edit  Tabs  Help
pi@raspberrypi:~ $ sudo i2cdetect -y 1
     0  1  2  3  4  5  6  7  8  9  a  b  c  d  e  f
00:          -- -- -- -- -- -- -- -- -- -- -- -- --
10: -- -- -- -- -- -- -- -- -- -- -- -- -- -- -- --
20: -- -- -- -- -- -- -- -- -- -- -- -- -- -- -- --
30: -- -- -- -- -- -- -- -- -- -- -- -- -- -- -- --
40: -- -- -- -- -- -- -- -- -- -- -- -- -- -- -- --
50: -- -- -- -- -- -- -- -- -- -- -- -- -- -- -- --
60: -- -- -- -- -- -- -- -- 68 -- -- -- -- -- -- --
70: -- -- -- -- -- -- -- --
pi@raspberrypi:~ $
```

Figure 10-4: I2C matrix display.

for your RTC chip. Here are the steps:
1. Open a terminal session.
2. Open the system config file with: sudo nano /boot/config.txt
3. Scroll to the bottom of the file that opens and add the line: dtoverlay=i2c-rtc,ds3231
4. NB: If you have a PCF8523 based RTC, replace ds3231 with pcf8523
5. Press Ctl-X followed by Y to close and save the file.
6. Reboot the Pi and run: sudo i2cdetect -y 1
7. This time, you should see UU displayed at the intersection of 60 and 8.

At this point, the RTC is properly installed but is not being used as the time source for the Pi. This is because the Pi normally runs a small program that acts as a fake hardware clock. We need to uninstall the software and make some changes to stop the Pi looking for the fake clock. Open a terminal session and remove the fake-clock with:

```
sudo apt -y remove fake-hwclock
```

Now we can enable our RTC by opening and editing the hwclock file:

```
Enter: sudo nano /lib/udev/hwclock-set
```

Comment-out the following lines near the top of the file by adding a # at the start of each line so they look like this:

```
#if [ -e /run/system/system ; then

#exit 0

#fi
```

To complete the process, connect your Pi to the Internet and enter:

```
sudo hwclock -w
```

This will store the current Pi time into the RTC. To read the time use:

```
sudo hwclock -r
```

That completes the RTC installation and setting. If you are using the recommended DS3231 based clock you can expect an accuracy of around 1 second per week over the temperature range 0-40°C.

Using a GPS dongle as a time source

An alternative method of acquiring date and time information is to use a GPS USB dongle. These are usually available at very reasonable prices and provide a compact solution. In addition to providing a reasonably accurate timing source the dongle will also provide positional data that could be useful. Whilst GPS timing solutions are usually associated with precision timing applications this is not the case with a USB connected GPS dongle. To establish accurate time, two information feeds are used. The first is the National Maritime Electronics

Association (NMEA) serial data stream that contains the full date/time information along with the positional data. Because this data is usually streamed over a serial connection, the timing can't be relied on for μsec accuracy. The serial data is normally supplemented by a separate 1PPS (Pulse Per Second) line that marks the precise start of every second. It's the combination of the serial data and the PPS line that enables high precision timing. In the case of our USB connected dongle, there is another variable due to the way the processor, in a multitasking operating system, gathers incoming data. Despite these limitations a simple USB connected GPS dongle can provide a clock that is accurate to within 250ms.

Most USB GPS dongles should work with the Pi and my tests were done with a Diymall VK-172GPS.

The first step is to install some essential software, so open a terminal session and enter the following:

```
sudo apt - y install gpsd gpsd-clients python-gps chrony
```

One of the installed items, GPSD, is a daemon that will run the GPS as a background service but we need to make some changes to its configuration. Open a terminal session and enter the following:

```
sudo nano /etc/default/gpsd
```

Make sure the following lines are present and amend them where necessary:

```
START_DAEMON="true"
```

```
USBAUTO="true"
```

```
DEVICES="/dev/ttyACM0"
```

```
GPSD_OPTIONS="-n"
```

Press Ctl-X followed by Y to save and close the file.

Reboot the Pi so we can now check that the new services we added are running.

Enter: systemctl is-active gpsd and you should see the response 'active'. Do the same with chrony by entering: systemctl is-active chronyd

With all the basic services running, let's check that the GPS data is being received by using the tools we have just installed. We have three tools available, but you need to check that your dongle has a fix before you'll see any data with these tools. A fix is usually indicated by the status LED flashing once per second.

The three tools we installed were: CGPS, GPSMON and XGPS. The following 3 lines show how to run each program:

```
cgps -s
```

```
gpsmon -n
```

```
xgps
```

To exit each program, press Ctl-C or close the window. If you're seeing data in these applications, you can be confident that the GPS is successfully talking to the Pi.

For the next step, we need to link the GPS data to the Pi clock and we'll do that using the Chrony application we installed earlier. We start by updating the chrony configuration file as shown below:

1. Open a terminal session (Ctl-Alt-T)
2. Open the Chrony configuration with: sudo nano /etc/chrony/chrony. conf
3. Add the following line to the end of the file: refclock SHM0 offset 0.5 delay 0.2 refid NMEA
4. Enter Ctl-X followed by Y to close and save the file

That completes the configuration so you can now examine the clock sources used by Chrony by entering:

```
chronyc sources -v
```

In a typical response where the Pi has no Internet connection and is using the GPS dongle as its only source of timing, this is indicated by a #* next to the entry marked NMEA. In this case # indicates that NMEA is a local timing source whilst * shows that Chrony is synchronised to NMEA. If you run the same command with an Internet connection, you will see several Internet NTP sources listed and one will have been selected as the source. Chrony will not synchronise to the GPS dongle in the presence of an Internet connection because the Internet source will be more accurate. For a detailed view of Chrony's time tracking use the following:

```
chronyc tracking
```

Chrony usage notes:
In cases where there is a large gap between the Pi time and the reference time, Chrony will incrementally close the gap. This is done to avoid software failures that can occur if the system time suddenly jumps to a new value. However, you can force a step change by issuing the following command:

```
sudo chronyc makestep
```

You should also be aware that the desktop clock on the PIXEL desktop synchronises with the system time only every 5 minutes, so don't be concerned if it appears to be out-of-step after making changes to the system time.

Raspberry Pi Stratum 1 Time Server

As discussed in the previous section to provide the Pi with a precision timing reference, we need a dedicated GPS board that can supply a precision PPS feed in addition to the serial NMEA data. There are several options on the market and these instructions should work for most. The main variation between boards will be in the GPIO pin number used to connect the PPS line. For my system, I used the Uputronics Raspberry Pi+ GPS Expansion Board, **Figure 10-5**. This is fitted with a ublox MAX-M8Q positioning module along with a supercap to retain the settings when powered down. The GPS board mounts neatly on top of the Pi, taking its power and communication links directly from the GPIO pins. For accurate timing, it is important to have a strong

Figure 10-5: Uputronics Pi+ GPS expansion board. Supplies NMEA and PPS.

GPS signal and I recommend using a good external antenna. To adapt these instructions for other boards, you will probably only need to amend the GPIO pin number used for the PPS signal (line 5 in the following instructions).

Before we can make use of this board, we need to install a few tools and software libraries and I've shown the steps here:

1. Start with a fresh Raspbian image and open a terminal session (Ctl-Alt-T).
2. Update the image with: sudo apt update && sudo apt upgrade
3. Install software libraries with: sudo apt install -y pps-tools libcap-dev libssl-dev
4. Open the Pi configuration file with: sudo nano /boot/config.txt
5. In the text editor that opens add the following new line: dtoverlay=pps-gpio,gpiopin=18
6. Press Ctl-X followed by Y to close and save the configuration file.
7. Open the modules file with: sudo nano /etc/modules
8. Add the following new line: pps-gpio
9. Press Ctl-X followed by Y to close and save the modules file.

The final change to the Pi configuration can be done as follows:

1. From the Pi menu, select Preferences - Raspberry Pi Configuration.
2. Select the Interfaces tab.
3. Set Serial Port to enabled.
4. Set Serial Console to disabled.

You can now reboot the Pi and check that the correct module has been loaded by opening a terminal session and entering: lsmod | grep pps

This should produce a couple of lines reporting pps_gpio and pps_core.

At this point, we need to check that the GPS is working and talking to the

Pi. Power-up the Pi with the GPS board mounted, and a GPS antenna connected. The GPS board will indicate GPS lock by the timepulse LED flashing at 1 pulse per second. If this is the first time the GPS has been powered-up, you may have to wait several minutes for the GPS chip to locate itself and achieve lock. When lock is secured you can check the PPS connection by entering the following in a terminal session:

```
sudo ppstest /dev/pps0
```

This should give you a response that prints every second and has fields for source, assert, sequence and clear. If you don't see that go back and check the previous steps and make sure your GPS board is properly seated on the GPIO pins. To exit this test, press: Ctl-C

That completes the GPS board configuration and the tests we've completed show that the PPS feed is working. The next stage is to add software to process the serial GPS data feed. To do that, enter the following line in a terminal session:

sudo apt install -y chrony gpsd gpsd-clients python-gps python-gi-cairo

This line installs Chrony, which is the time server, along with Gpsd, which is a GPS daemon that will manage the GPS data in the background. Gpsd is a remarkable application that's gained universal adoption as the go-to software for handling GPS data. It is used extensively in everything from mobile phones to robotics! Before we can check that Gpsd is working, we must edit the configuration file. To do that enter: sudo nano /etc/default/gpsd and edit the file that opens to make sure the following lines are present:

```
START_DAEMON="true"

USBAUTO="false"

DEVICES="/dev/serial0 /dev/pps0"

GPSD_OPTIONS="-n"

GPSD_SOCKET="/var/run/gpsd.sock"

Press Ctl-X followed by Y to save and close the file.
```

Reboot the Pi and enter the following two commands in a terminal session and they should both display 'active':

```
systemctl is-active gpsd

systemctl is-active chronyd
```

Fixing GPSD start-up:
You may find that GPSD reports as inactive. This is because the version of GPSD in the Raspbian repository doesn't automatically start as it should. Fortunately, it can be fixed by adding a symbolic link as shown here:

Open a terminal session and enter the following as a single line:

```
sudo ln -s /lib/systemd/system/gpsd.service /etc/sys-
temd/system/multi-user.target.wants/
```

Reboot the Pi and you can check that the GPS NMEA data is being received using the tools we have just installed. Open a terminal session and any of the following commands should produce results (Ctl-C to exit):

```
xgps
```

```
cgps -s
```

```
gpsmon -n
```

At this point, we have tested both the PPS and NMEA data feeds, so we can be confident that the appropriate data is reaching the Pi. The final stage is to use the timeserver, Chrony, to combine the two data streams and transform the Pi into a Stratum 1 Time Server. You may have seen other tutorials that use NTP as the time server but Chrony is a better fit for the Raspberry Pi. This is because Chrony is fully compatible with NTP but has been designed to cope with long periods of off-line use. That better matches the Pi usage as, in many Pi applications, the GPS maybe the only timing source available.

To configure Chrony, we need to open its configuration file using the following from a terminal session:

```
sudo nano /etc/chrony/chrony.conf
```

Edit the file that opens to match this:

```
pool 2.debian.pool.ntp.org iburst auto_offline
```

```
keyfile /etc/chrony/chrony.keys
```

```
driftfile /var/lib/chrony/chrony.drift
```

```
logdir /var/log/chrony
```

```
makestep 1 3
```

```
allow
```

```
refclock SHM 0 refid NMEA precision 1e-1 offset 0.9999 de-
lay 0.2
```

```
refclock PPS /dev/pps0 refid PPS
```

When you've finished editing the file, press Ctl-X followed by Y to save and close the file. Before we move on to the testing, I'll explain a few of the lines in the Chrony configuration file. The first line points to a pool of online NTP servers that will be used when available. The iburst suffix sets the server polling rate to 2 seconds, whilst auto_offline will mark a server as offline if it fails to respond to 2 consecutive requests. Normally, Chrony will gradually alter the system time to match the network time. However, the makestep 1 3 tells Chrony to do a step update for the first 3 updates if the difference between network and system time is 1 second or more. Without this, Chrony could take hours to catchup if the system time is a long way off.

That completes Chrony configuration so you can reboot the Pi and start testing.

Testing and monitoring the time server

Whilst implementing this server, we have installed several monitoring tools that can now be used to make sure everything is working as expected.

Test 1:
Boot-up the Pi with the GPS board and antenna connected but with no network (LAN or Wi-Fi). Wait for the GPS board to acquire lock. This is usually signified by the 1PPS LED flashing at 1 Pulse Per Second. Enter the following command:

```
chronyc sources -v
```

This will produce a tabulated display showing the timing sources being used by Chrony. The -v option in this command provides a verbose output that includes an explanation of each field. This is displayed at the top of the output. If all is well, you will see NMEA and PPS listed. A while after power-up, you will see an asterisk appear adjacent to the NMEA entry. The asterisk shows which of the available servers are being used by Chrony as its timing reference. The asterisk will eventually move to the PPS entry, which is where we want it. The changeover may take a long time.

Test 2:
For this test, we'll use the tracking option along with the Shell watch command to monitor the way Chrony is interacting with the Pi. With the Internet still disconnected, reboot the Pi and enter the following in a terminal session:

```
watch -n 1 chronyc -m sources tracking
```

Immediately after powerup, the Ref time (UTC) row will display 'Thu Jan 01 00:00:00 1970' and NMEA and PPS entries will have #? in the left-hand column. After a few minutes, the time and date will update, and an asterisk will appear next to the NMEA entry. After a few more minutes, Chrony should again conclude that the PPS is more accurate and start using that source as indicated by the asterisk.

Test 3:
In this test we'll see how Chrony performs when Internet NTP servers are available. First reconnect the Internet (LAN or Wi-Fi) and restart the Pi. When it finishes booting, run the tracking monitor again:

```
watch -n 1 chronyc -m sources tracking
```

This time, the clock will update quickly but one of the Internet servers

Command	Description
`sudo date -s "Aug 7 09:15"`	Manually sets the system date & time and is useful when testing RTC and GPS units.
`sudo hwclock -w`	This command updates the RTC with the current system time. Use this when you are connected to a network and want to force the RTC to sync with network/system time.
`sudo hwclock -r`	This displays the current RTC time and is useful for checking the RTC
`sudo hwclock - s`	Sets the system time from the RTC
`sudo hwclock -set -date "8/11/18 15:24:00"`	Manually sets the RTC time and date – useful for testing
`sudo timedatectl`	Displays the status of all the Pi clock sources
`sudo chronyc makestep`	Forces the system time to make a step change to the reference time ie GPS. This avoids the time lag caused by chrony incrementally adjusting the clock.

Table 10-1: Time related commands.

will probably be shown as the source. After a few minutes, Chrony will again determine that PPS is its most accurate source and it will select PPS as the source.

Test 4:

For this final test we'll check that Chrony reverts to an Internet timeserver if the GPS signal is lost. Start the Pi with Internet connected and run the tracking command again:

```
watch -n 1 chronyc -m sources tracking
```

Leave the Pi running until PPS has been selected as the source and has the asterisk marker. Now, disconnect the GPS antenna and check that the 1 PPS LED on the GPS board has stopped blinking. Chrony should eventually switch back to one of the Internet timeservers. However, this will only occur when the difference between the system time and the network time exceeds the preset threshold. As the Pi clock is quite stable, it can take several hours to switch. This slow changeover is deliberately set to avoid the clock jitter that would occur if Chrony was to keep switching between NTP servers. To force a switch, you can manually adjust the system time. I suggest moving the time forwards by a couple of minutes using the following command:

```
sudo d-ate +T% -s "11:42:00"
```

This sudden change will jolt Chrony to abandon all the current timeservers and recommence the synchronisation. To check for a natural changeover, just remove the GPS antenna and leave it for a few hours. You should find Chrony will automatically reselect one of the online sources.

Another useful monitoring command is chronyc sourcestats This produces a table, showing the historic timing performance of all the current sources.

Summary

In this section I've taken you through the most common time keeping solutions for the Pi. Despite its small size and low-cost a Pi with a suitable GPS HAT is able to perform well as a Quantum-1 Time Server and makes an ideal timing source for the workshop.

Powering the Pi

A dependable power source is essential for reliable operation of the Pi, so in this chapter, I'll take you through a range of options that have worked well for me.

Mains power

By far the easiest and most popular power supply for the Pi is a plug-top mains power unit. These are available at very reasonable prices (under £10) and are easy to use. If you're unsure what to go for, I suggest using one of the official Pi power supplies. These are designed specifically for the Pi and usually have an output voltage of 5.1V and a current capacity depending on the Pi model. The 2A version is fine for all models except the Pi-3B, Pi-3B+ and Pi-3A+, where a 2.5A or 3A supply is recommended. The 5.1V output voltage of the official units is to help compensate for the voltage-drop in the USB power cable and the micro USB socket.

Choosing micro USB cables

If you're using a power source that employs a separate USB cable, some care is required. Many of today's USB cables are designed more for style and convenience rather than performance. As a result, they use very thin conductors (giving a higher resistance) that can severely limit their usefulness as a power cable. It's not uncommon to see a combined cable and connector resistance of 0.3Ω or more. That may not sound like much but if the power supply is delivering 5.0V at 1.5A, the voltage drop will be 0.45V leaving the Pi with just 4.55V, which is too low. To help you spot power problems, the Pi has a power warning system in the form of an icon that appears at the top right of the screen. On earlier systems, the

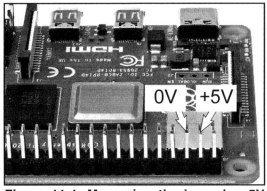

Figure 11-1: Measuring the incoming 5V supply at the GPIO pins.

icon was a small rainbow coloured square, but the latest system uses a lightning bolt to indicate power supply problems. When choosing micro USB cable for your Pi, I suggest you get one that's designed for fast-charging smartphones. These high-speed charging models can draw up to 2.4A so those cables will normally be ideal for the Pi. You can easily check the voltage that's reaching the Pi by connecting a digital voltmeter between GPIO pins 2 and 6, see Figure 11-1.

Processors and battery power

Let's start with a cautionary warning. Microprocessors in general, are extremely reliable when powered by a well-regulated supply of the correct voltage. However, one thing they really don't like is a supply that gradually dwindles to below its safe operating voltage, ie a typical unregulated battery supply. Operating below the minimum voltage will initially cause the Pi to become unreliable with an assortment of random data errors. This can lead to corruption of the SD card and a Pi that won't boot. This type of voltage related failure is commonly known as a brown-out. The Pi includes voltage regulators that will shut-down at the critical voltage but I've seen unreliable performance when the supply voltage approaches that trigger point. The simple solution is to use a modern switch-mode regulator between the battery supply and the Pi. These regulators will maintain the correct voltage to the Pi as the battery voltage declines. When the regulator reaches the point where it can no longer maintain the 5V supply, it simply cuts the output completely. Whilst that will also crash the Pi, it is usually far less troublesome than a brown-out.

Micro USB vs GPIO pins

There are two main methods used to connect external power to your Pi. The safest and most common is to use the micro USB socket as this includes overcurrent, reverse polarity and transient spike protection. The alternative is to supply power via pins 2 (+5V) and pin 6 (ground) of the GPIO connector. Whilst the GPIO option works well, it bypasses some of the protection, thus leaving the Pi vulnerable. I'll show you how to deal with this later in this chapter.

Pi built-in protection

The power protection built into the Pi power supply has changed significantly since the original Pi, but it's useful to understand the Pi protection systems when considering your power options. All the Pi models A and B up to and including

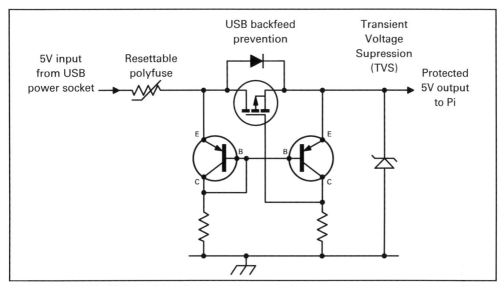

Figure 11-2: Pi USB backfeed protection circuit.

the Pi-3B featured 3 protection devices as shown in **Figure 11-2**. The first was a self-resettable Polyfuse to protect against over-current. All the early models used a 2-amp device but the Pi-3B and B+ models have a 2.5A Polyfuse. For overvoltage and transient suppression, a TVS (Transient Voltage Suppression) diode is used and all models except the Zeros have this fitted. The TVS device has a peak surge current of 65 amps and triggers at a voltage of 6.5 to 7 volts. In between the Polyfuse and the TVS is an interesting circuit comprising a pair of transistors and a MOSFET. These are configured to operate as a very low-volt-drop power-diode. This is to prevent a GPIO connected external power supply from back-feeding through the micro USB connector. The power diode circuit is fitted to all models except the, Pi-4B, 3B+ and Zero models. It's important to note that the two Zero models have no on-board power supply protection. I've shown the Pi power protection by model in **Table 11-1**.

Pi Model	Polyfuse Rating (Trip current)	Power Diode Fitted?	Transient protection
B+	2A	Y	SMBJ5.0A
A+	2A (4A)	Y	"
2B	2A(4A)	Y	"
3B	2.5A (5A)	Y	"
3B+	2.5A (5A)	N	"
4B	Not fitted	N	"
Zero & Zero-W	Not fitted	N	Not fitted
Zero-W	Not fitted	N	None

Table 11-1.

Phone power packs

Probably the simplest and most cost-effective battery solution for the Pi is to use one of the Li-Po (Lithium Polymer) mobile phone power-packs that you'll find available from all the usual online suppliers. These are available in a wide range of capacities up to more than 24,000mAh or 24Ah! These power-packs include all the necessary control circuitry both to charge the internal batteries and to maintain a reliable 5V supply as the power is drained. I've carried-out many tests on these power packs and they have all behaved extremely well. In each case, the 5V supply was regulated to within a few tens of millivolts right up to the abrupt cut-off as the battery reached its minimum safe discharge capacity.

In practice, the power available from phone power-packs is about 80% of the advertised capacity. This is because it's common practice to quote the input power required to charge the power-pack rather than the discharge power that it can supply.

Vehicle supplies

When powering a Pi from a vehicle, the simplest solution is often to use a phone charger that connects to the cigar lighter socket in the car. These are readily available at very attractive prices, but you need to check that it is specified to deliver the current required by your Pi project. A 2A rated device will be fine for most Pi projects. If you have a more modern car with a USB power socket that can also be used.

If neither of those options fit the bill, it's very easy to build your own vehicle power unit. I suggest you use a switch-mode, buck converter, as these are the most efficient way to handle the voltage conversion from the vehicle's 13.8V down to 5V. Modern switch-mode converters can provide efficiencies of 90% or more, so you won't need a separate heat sink. I've used the Recom R-78B-2.0

Figure 11-3: Recom R-78B-2.0 switch mode regulator for 12V power sources.

devices successfully for many of my projects, **Figure 11-3**. This device costs around £7 and is a complete 5V, 2A buck converter and regulator with just three connections: input, output and ground. The R-78B series operates with minimal external components, so it's a very attractive solution. Regulation is within ±0.25% and efficiency, for the 5V output variant with a 12V supply is 90%, giving a heat dissipation of about 100mW, hence no heatsink.

If you're building your own solution, overcurrent protection is essential. Vehicle batteries are designed to deliver hundreds of amps to a starter motor, so a short circuit to ground in your feed cable has the potential to cause a serious fire if not properly protected. The simplest solution is, either to use one of the vehicle's accessory supply lines or fit an in-line fuse (3A) at the battery end of the connecting cable.

Li-Po cells

An alternative approach, for a low-power project, is to use a single 3.7V Li-Po cell as your power source. Single cells are used extensively in the model making world, so there are plenty available in a variety of sizes and capacities at very low cost. Buying a cheap single-cell Li-Po battery is usually a better option than buying cheap multi-cell batteries. This is because the useful life of cheap, multi-cell, Li-Po batteries is often compromised by poor matching of the component cells. This inevitably results in one cell being overcharged that shortens its life and carries a fire risk. This problem doesn't occur with single cells, providing you use a dedicated Li-Po charger. The voltage range of a single cell Li-Po battery is 3.7V to 4.2V, which is just below the voltage we need for the Pi. The simple solution here is to use a switch-mode, boost converter, to bring the voltage up to 5V and provide the required regulation. Because the voltage conversion from a single Li-Po is useful for lots of other projects, you will find several ready-made solutions on the market. These usually include a dedicated Li-Po charging circuit as well as a 5V boost supply, so giving a complete and very compact solution. A popular example for Pi-Zero projects is the Adafruit PowerBoost 1000. Alternatively, the Pimoroni Wide Input SHIM, **Figure 11-4**, provides a stable 5V at up to 2A from a single LiPo cell though you would need a separate charger. For a complete, ready-to-go solution, the PiJuice HAT takes some beating. This fits directly on the Pi and is available with a range of replaceable battery capacities from 1.3Ah through to 12Ah.

As is the case with car batteries, Li-Po cells have a very low internal resistance and can supply huge currents under fault conditions, so it's important to include overcurrent protection at the point of connection to the battery. A simple fuse will do but I often use a Polymeric Positive Temperature Coefficient (PPTC or polyfuse) resettable fuse as they cost less than 20p each and do the job very well. A good choice for Pi projects is the Multicomp MC36253, a small, wire-ended, device with a holding current of 2.5A but will it trip at 5A. The DC resistance at room temperature is just 0.02Ω so has a very low volt drop (0.02V at 1A). An alternative would be the Bourns MF-LSMF260X surface mount device. These are very cheap (£0.30) and can be easily connected in series with a power lead and protected with heat shrink sleeving, **Figure 11-5**.

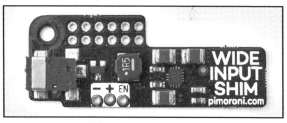

Figure 11-4: Wide input Power Shim for the Pi.

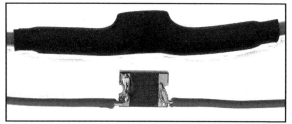

Figure 11-5: DIY polyfuse protection for the Pi. The polyfuse is protected with heat-shrink sleeving.

Alkaline batteries

There are cases when alkaline batteries are the best choice, and this can be particularly true if there are unlikely to be any charging facilities locally. As mentioned at the start of this section, it's not practical to use battery power without a voltage regulator because the Pi requires a well-regulated constant voltage supply. For the few occasions when I've used alkaline batteries, I opted for 6 AA cells together with the Recom R-78B-2.0 regulator to provide the regulated 5V output. You could also use the excellent Pimoroni Wide Input SHIM.

Pi Power over Ethernet

There will be times when you need to power a remotely located Pi. Typical examples could be a Pi based security camera or maybe as an SDR radio server. In both these cases, Ethernet is the preferred network connection but providing a power supply can be a problem. This is where Power over Ethernet (PoE) comes to the rescue. The technology is well established and has been used extensively on commercial premises to power, Ethernet switches, security cameras, Voice over IP (VoIP) phones, etc. PoE operates using a technique known as phantom power. In this system the DC supply is connected via centre-taps on the data transformers, **Figure 11-6**. This causes the current to flow equally in both wires, so it doesn't degrade the balanced, data signal. This technique also has the benefit of reducing the DC resistance.

There are two parts to providing PoE. The first is a central Ethernet node, usually a switch, that provides the power source and injects the supply onto the Ethernet cables. One of the design problems for PoE is dealing with the small conductor size of standard Cat-5 Ethernet cable. This cable was designed to carry data signals so uses relatively thin conductors with a maximum current rating of 0.6A. That's a significant limitation when we want to have up to 2.5A available for the Pi. The solution is to inject a higher voltage, usually 48V at

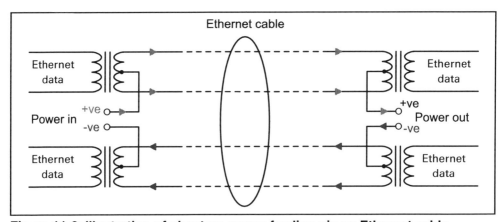

Figure 11-6: Illustration of phantom power feeding via an Ethernet cable.

the feed point and use efficient, switch-mode, buck regulators to down-convert to whatever voltage the terminal equipment needs. The power rating for Type 1 PoE is just over 15W per outlet that gives a conductor current of around 0.3A; comfortably within the cable and connector ratings. To

Figure 11-7: Dedicated Pi PoE HAT.

power a remote Pi, we ideally need 5V at up to 2.5A. Application of Ohms Law shows that the 15W PoE capacity stepped down to 5V would give 3A, just what we need for powering the Pi.

Setting-up PoE: To use commercial PoE units with the Pi, we first need a source of PoE power. The simplest solution is to fit a PoE enabled Ethernet switch at a convenient point in your network. PoE uses standard network cables so there's no change in the cabling. Just one point to remember. Cat-5 or Cat-6 cable that's normally used for network cabling and has four pairs of wires. I have seen cheap Chinese Ethernet patch cables that use two-pair cable. Whilst these will handle 100Mb/s data, they may not support Gigabit and PoE as all four pairs are usually required. At the Pi end of the link, we need a switching regulator to generate the 5V for the Pi. If you are using a Pi-3B+ or Pi-4B, the simplest and tidiest solution is to buy the Pi PoE HAT, **Figure 11-7**. This mounts on top of the Pi and feeds the correct power to the Pi with no additional wiring. For other Pi models, there is another, more expensive, PoE HAT available.

The cheaper alternative is to use an Active PoE splitter of the correct rating. There are plenty available from online sellers for around (£10). You will need an active splitter that provides an output of 5V at around 2A for the Pi 2 and 3 models, but you could use a lower current version for Pi-Zero based applications. The TP-link TL-PoE-10R shown in **Figure 11-8** provides a switchable output of 5V, 9V or 12V with the 5V output able to deliver up to 2 amps that is ideal.

Figure 11-8: TP-Link TL-PoE-10R PoE Extractor with switchable output voltage.

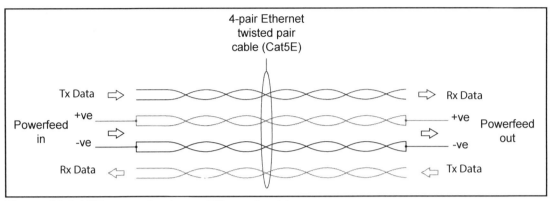

Figure 11-9: DIY power feed over Ethernet cable.

Do it Yourself PoE

All Pi models except the Pi-3B+ and 4B use 100Mb/s Ethernet that only requires two pairs of the four-pair CAT-5 or 6 cable, thus leaving the other two pairs spare. We are free to use these spare pairs to carry DC power to the Pi. Before we get too carried away, we need to look at the current handling capabilities of the cable. The CAT-5 specification quotes a maximum current per conductor of just under 0.6A and the DC resistance is 0.188Ω per m. As we have two spare pairs available, we could bunch the wires of each pair to halve the DC resistance and double the current capacity. Let's see how a 10m run of CAT-5 cable would look. By bunching the pairs, we halve the resistance to 0.094Ω / metre or 0.94Ω for a 10m cable length. However, we need two bunched pairs so the combined loop resistance will double to 1.88Ω, **Figure 11-9**. If we assume a modest Pi current consumption of 1A, that would give a voltage drop in the cable of 1.88V. That means we would need to inject 6.88V to get 5V at the Pi. Not only is that an awkward value but the Pi current draw varies significantly so the applied voltage will vary proportionately. The answer is to follow commercial practice and inject a higher voltage and use an efficient switching regulator at the Pi end to deliver a regulated 5 volts. The natural voltage choice for an amateur radio shack, would be to use a 13.8V supply. Connecting the 13.8V supply to the Ethernet cable is done using a device called a passive PoE injector. These are readily available from online suppliers and are usually sold as an injector and extractor pair, **Figure 11-10**. A word of warning!

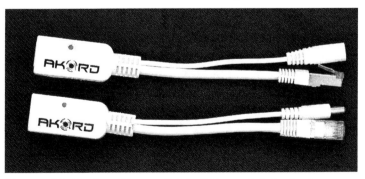

Figure 11-10: Readily available Ethernet injector/extractor pairs.

Don't connect your high current shack supply directly to the injector because a fault on the Ethernet cable could easily start a fire. Either use a standard fuse rated at 1.5A or use a Polyfuse as described earlier in this chapter. At the Pi end of the Cat-5 cable, you will need a PoE extractor and a buck regulator to reduce the voltage to a regulated 5V DC. I recommend the Recom R-78B-2.0 module as it's proven to be very reliable for me but there are plenty of other choices. For a ready-built solution the Pimoroni Wide Input SHIM is an excellent little device that connects to the GPIO pins and accept voltages from 3 to 16 volts.

GPIO power feeding

As I mentioned earlier in this chapter, it is possible to power the Pi by supplying 5V DC directly to GPIO pins 1/2 and 6. When fed in this way, the TVS diode (where fitted) is still connected and will protect against transient voltages, **Figure 11-11**. However, when faced with an overvoltage fault, the TVS diode will switch-on to a near short circuit but relies on blowing a fuse to safely disconnect the supply. If there's no fuse in the feed, the TVS diode will quickly burn-out and could allow the over voltage condition to reach the Pi. This failure can be avoided by adding add a standard glass/ceramic wire fuse or a polyfuse in the supply feed, **Figure 11-12**. Polyfuses are a good option as they are very compact and automatically reset when the fault condition is removed. I suggest you select a polyfuse

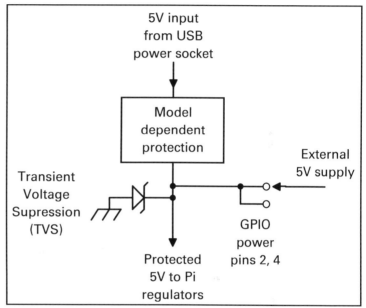

Figure 11-11: Simplified wiring of the TVS diode.

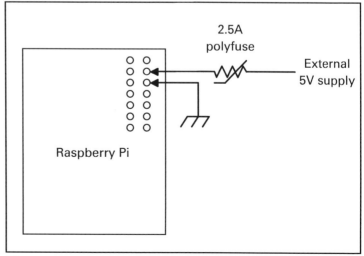

Figure 11-12: Wiring suggestion for polyfuse protection.

with a 2.5A holding current and the lowest hold resistance. One that I've used for many projects is the wire-ended Multicomp MC36253.

Summary

In this chapter we've covered a wide range of power options for the Pi and I hope you now have the knowledge to choose the best power solution for your application. Do be careful to add good over-current protection when using high-current sources such as Li-Po batteries or your main workshop supply.

Displays

There are a huge range of display systems out there so, in this chapter, I'll cover my experiences with a few of the popular solutions from the Pi Foundation and 3rd party suppliers.

First Rule – Avoid the composite video output

I say this simply because the Pi was designed to provide HD and UHD (Pi-4 only) quality video via the HDMI port and includes a dedicated Graphics Processing Unit (GPU) for that task. In situations when HDMI is not available, the Pi provides a, lower quality, composite video output. This video output supports the old 625-line TV standard, so provides much lower resolution than the 1920 x 1080 pixel resolution of an HD image or 3840 x 2160 pixels of UHD on the Pi-4. If you need to use the composite video, I'll show you how to access it later in this chapter.

HDMI

One design requirement of the Raspberry Pi, that has remained constant through all the model iterations, is its support for full-HD video. Thanks to the on-board graphics processor, all Pi models have been able to supply full-HD quality video output over its HDMI connector. As a result, a standard HD monitor or TV is the best display option for the Raspberry Pi. This standard was originally chosen to support the Pi's primary role as a learning tool for young students. With the proliferation of video games, most of the target audience were likely to have an HD TV or monitor around the house that could be used with the Raspberry Pi, thus saving the additional expense of a new monitor. In cases where a new monitor was required, the market for HD monitors and TVs is very competitive, so excellent prices can be had from high street retailers.

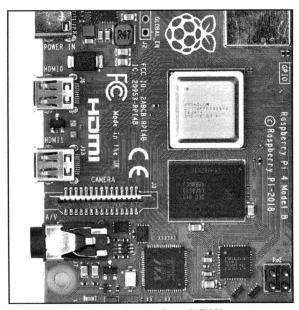

Figure 12-1: Pi-4B dual micro-HDMI ports.

Prior to the launch of the Pi-4 a full-size HDMI socket was used on all Model A and B units. Due to their diminutive size, the Pi-Zeros range use a mini-HDMI socket. The Pi-4 has seen a significant video performance boost and provides two micro-HDMI sockets that support resolutions up to UHD (4k), **Figure 12-1**. With one UHD monitor connected it can manage 60 FPS but when running two UHD monitors the frame rate drops to a, still respectable, 30 FPS. In addition to conventional, large screen monitors, there are many small-screen HDMI monitors on the market that can be used with the Pi. However, please take note of the following section on small screen limitations before diving in.

Small screen HDMI monitors

The increasing use of digital cameras for video work combined with the development of drones has created a demand for small-screen, battery powered, HD and 4k compatible monitors that can plug directly into the camera or drone controller's HDMI port. Providing they use the HDMI standard these screens can also be used directly with the Raspberry Pi and generally work very well. Lilliput are one of the prominent manufacturers in this field and have an extensive range of good value monitors available. As the video market is moving towards 4k or 8k formats, you will often see basic HD monitors advertised at very attractive prices. In addition to being good HDMI monitors, these units are designed for field use so are usually very robust, offer a wide viewing angle, and can be battery powered. The most common battery power source being the Sony NP-F970 format 7.2V at 7.8Ah battery units. These field monitors can often be powered from a standard 12V vehicle supply, so are ideal for use in the car or caravan.

One important aspect of all small screens, that often leads to disappointment, is readability. If you connect a 7" HDMI monitor to the Pi, the entire Pixel desktop will be displayed on the 7" screen, exactly as it is on a larger monitor - only much smaller. That can make the text and icons unreadable and menus difficult to navigate! One way to deal with this, is to make use of the Pixel-Doubling option that's available to Pi-3B+ and earlier models. When activated, this draws each pixel of the original image as a square block of four pixels, thus doubling the number of pixels in each direction. The resulting screen resolution becomes approximately 960 x 540 pixels. This works extremely well for many programs, but only if the user interface has been designed to operate within a 960 x 540 pixel window. If you use Pixel-Doubling with software intended for a desktop environment, you may well find that the Graphic User Interface (GUI) overflows the screen and cannot be resized to fit. Examples of this problem can be seen in the amateur radio software FLDIGI and WSJT-X. At the time of writing, neither of these programs are able work successfully with pixel doubling activated on a HD resolution monitor. This is because the GUI (Graphic User Interface) cannot be reduced to fit within the 960 x 540 pixel screen resolution. In my experience and depending on your eyesight, I find a 10.1" display is the minimum workable size for a full resolution HD desktop.

Viewing your Pi desktop with a tablet

Once you start looking at displays of 10.1" or more, the price and power can become a problem. An alternative solution is to use a cheap tablet. There are lots of 10.1" tablets available on the second-hand market and you may well find friends or relatives have an old one kicking around. Hacking the tablet to access the screen is possible but a much easier solution is to make use of Virtual Network Computing (VNC). This is a graphical desktop sharing system that lets us view and interact with a remote computer, **Figure 12-2**. The standard Pi operating system includes RealVNC that is a well-respected VNC application that makes it very easy to view the Pi desktop on another tablet or computer. Whilst this is most often used for diagnostic purposes, in this case, VNC provides a way to view the Pi desktop and operate its software from a standard tablet. Whilst this can be done over the wider Internet, the technique I'm describing here is for accessing a Pi that's connected to the same local network as the tablet. In addition to providing a useful and cheap way to view the Pi desktop, you also retain the tablet's touch-controlled zooming to magnify any difficult to read screen areas. Whilst it is also possible to navigate software and use the onscreen keyboard, I find it much easier to use a separate Bluetooth keyboard/mouse combination. All tablets feature Bluetooth so it's very easy to add a mouse/keyboard combina-

Figure 12-2: WSJT-X on the Pi controlled by a Samsung tablet using RealVNC.

tion. Here's a step-by-step guide to using VNC.

1. With the Pi running and the desktop displayed, use the Pi menu button (top left) to select Preferences – Raspberry Pi Configuration.
2. In the configuration panel select the Interfaces tab.
3. You will see VNC listed as one of the options, click the Enable button.
4. Click OK to complete the activation.

That completes the Pi configuration and you should see the VNC logo showing in the top right of the status bar. The next step is to install the free RealVNC viewer on your tablet or smartphone:

1. Go to the Play Store or App Store and search/install RealVNC viewer.(For a Windows Tablet or PC the RealVNC Viewer is downloaded from the realvnc.com website).
2. Once installed, open RealVNC Viewer.
3. Click the + icon to add a new computer.
4. Enter the IP address of the Pi you want to control.
5. Select connect
6. You will be prompted for the username and password of your Pi.

That completes the connection and you should now have full control of the Pi. Whilst the connection technique I've described here is limited to devices on your local network, RealVNC also facilitates full remote access over the Internet. To use this service, you need access to RealVNC's cloud services and the good news is that Raspberry Pi owners get a free account for up to 5 computers. To take advantage of this offer, you need to create a free account on the RealVNC website at: www.realvnc.com.

High resolution - 4k and beyond monitors

4k UHD monitors and TVs are becoming common place, but you can only really take advantage of that higher resolution using a Pi-4. For the other Pi models, HD (1920 x 1080 pixels) is the optimum output resolution. If you connect a Pi-3+ or older Pi to a UHD monitor, the Pi screen will be displayed as a small rectangle on the screen, unless your monitor automatically upscales the image to fit UHD dimensions. It is technically possible to push the Pi-3 up to resolutions as high as 3840 x 2160 pixels (UHD), but this requires overclocking the processor. The lack of a hardware decoder for these higher resolutions also means the processor has to handle all the video decoding in software, so you will need to reduce the frame rate to lighten the load. The net result is poor video quality and very few processing cycles available for other applications! If you want to use UHD resolution you really need to upgrade to a Pi-4B.

In cases where the monitor doesn't automatically upscale your HD output to fill the screen, you can use the Pixel-Doubling I mentioned earlier. This pushes the 1920 x 1080 image up to 3840 x 2160 pixels that will fill a 4k screen. When activated, you will see a HD quality image on your high-res display. Without pixel doubling or up-scaling in the monitor, the Pi's HD output would only occupy a small area of the screen.

Activating pixel-doubling:

The simplest way to activate pixel doubling is to use the Pi configuration tool. Here's a step-by-step guide. NB: Pixel doubling is only available for Pi-3B+ and earlier models.

1. Left-click the Pi menu and select Preferences – Raspberry Pi Configuration.
2. On the System tab you will see the pixel doubling entry.
3. Click the radio button for Enabled.
4. Click Ok.
5. You will then be told that the Pi must be rebooted to enable pixel doubling.

It's as simple as that! When the Pi reboots you should see that everything is displayed at double the normal size. To revert to normal operation, repeat the process but set the pixel doubling radio button to Disable.

Pi-4 dual HDMI outputs

The Pi-4B is the first Pi model to support dual video outputs with UHD (4k) resolution. This is a major step forward that makes the Pi feel like a real contender as a desktop PC. As with the earlier Pi models, identification of the connected HDMI monitors occurs during the boot process, so you need to ensure your monitors are connected before you power-up. One important point to note here is that the highest resolution monitor should always be connected to HDMI-1, which is the port closest to the USB-C power socket. If you don't do this, you may find that the full resolution for that monitor is not available in the options. The new screen configuration panel is only available when using a Pi-4 or any other Pi model with dual HDMI outputs. You will also find that the pixel doubling option is hidden when using a Pi-4. This is likely to be a temporary omission pending an update to OpenGL. You can find the screen configuration panel via the Preference menu, under Screen Configuration. From this tool, you can control which screen is the primary and set the resolution of each screen independently. Also included is a graphic interface that lets you reposition the coverage of the two screens and control the amount of separation or overlap. The dual HDMI controls work very well and let you use an extended desktop even when mixing 4k and HD resolution monitors.

How to use the Composite Video Output

In the early Pi versions, the composite output was delivered via a standard RCA phono socket. However, as the Pi has grown, PCB space has been at a premium, so the phono socket has been replaced by a dual-purpose 4-pole 3.5mm jack,

Audio and composite video jack

Figure 12-3: Pi4B audio/composite video jack.

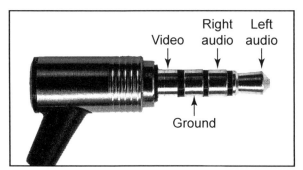

Right Left
Video audio audio

Ground

Figure 12-4: Wiring for the audio/composite video jack.

Figure 12-3. This jack now handles the stereo audio output and the composite video. Whilst this is a great space saver, it has caused some confusion because the 4-pole jack is used by many phone suppliers to combine audio and video signals but there are several different wiring schemes. I've shown a diagram of the Pi wiring scheme in **Figure 12-4**. Here you can see that the video signal is connected to the sleeve whilst the ground or return is available on ring 2. Although the connectors can be a bit fiddley to wire, it's quite possible to make your own leads. If you'd rather purchase ready-made leads, I recommend that you purchase from a Pi dealer to ensure you have the correct wiring configuration.

The Pi automatically selects HDMI or composite video output at boot time by testing for the presence of a valid HDMI device. If an HDMI device is detected, that is used as the output device. However, if there's no HDMI device, the Pi automatically reverts to composite video. It's important to note, that the Pi only checks for HDMI devices at boot, so it won't automatically change from HDMI to composite or vice-versa if you plug/unplug an HDMI monitor. It's also important to be aware that there are two composite video standards in common use, PAL and NTSC. PAL is used mainly in the UK, Europe and Asia, whilst North America uses NTSC. If you are installing Raspbian using the official NOOBS package, you can force loading of the correct video system at boot by repeatedly pressing the number 3 for PAL or 4 for NTSC.

In cases where you have a running system and you want to force it to use composite video, you can do so by editing the Pi config.txt file. Here's a step-by-step guide:
1. Open a terminal session.
2. Enter: sudo nano /boot/config.txt
3. This will open the config.txt file in the Nano text editor.
4. Use the arrow keys to scroll down to the line: #sdtv_mode=2
5. Delete the # from the front of the line to force composite output using the PAL standard.
6. If you need NTSC output, change the line to: sdtv_mode=0
7. The default composite aspect ratio is 4:3.
8. To change the aspect ratio to 16:9, add this new line: sdtv_aspect=3

9. Press control + x followed by y then return to save the modified config.txt file.
10. Reboot the Pi for the changes to take effect.

Project displays

Whilst a full HD or UHD display can be very impressive, many Raspberry Pi projects only require a simple interface, so a more modest display solution is appropriate. The selection available for the Pi is extensive and extends from simple 2-line LCD units to 7" touch-screen displays. I'll cover a few popular examples here.

Small alphanumeric LCDs:
Small 16-character 2- and 4-line displays have been available for many years and can be picked up at very reasonable prices **Figure 12-5**. Whilst the original Hitachi HDD44780 LCD controller has long since ceased production, this interface standard has prevailed and the vast majority of 2- and 4-line LCD displays adhere to the HDD44780 standard. However, it's worth checking HDD44780 compatibility when purchasing because there are lots of code libraries available for that standard, so building the display into your project will be that much simpler. The cheapest way to use these displays is to hard-wire them directly to the Pi GPIO ports and I've shown a typical wiring diagram in **Figure 12-6**. One essential point to watch is that the Read/Write pin must be permanently tied to ground if you're using a 5V version of the display. This is to prevent the display from sending data back into the Pi. If this pin is not grounded, you could have 5V logic signals from the display being sent to the 3.3V Pi GPIO pins, which would damage the Pi processor. To use these popular displays with Python, you need to install the appropriate Python library. There are plenty to choose from, but my favourite is RPLCD that's available from

Figure 12-5: Adafruit 16 x 2 LCD module for the Pi.

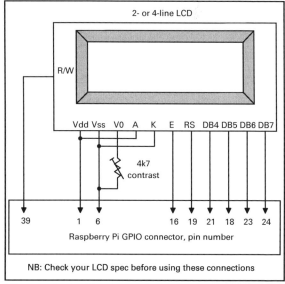

Figure 12-6: Typical direct connection for a 2-line LCD unit.

pypi.org and can be installed on the Pi as follows:

1. Open a terminal window
2. Enter: sudo pip install RPLCD

This will automatically download and install the library for you. Once installed, the library is very simple to use, and full documentation can be found by searching for RPLCD on the pypi site. Here are a few examples to get you started.

To set the position of the cursor and therefore the start position of the text use: lcd.cursor_pos(r, c) where r and c are the row and column numbers. These count from 0, so the first column of the first line is lcd.cursor_posn(0, 0).

To show a text string on the display use:

```
lcd.write_string('Hello')
```

To clear the display, use

```
lcd.clear()
```

The RPLCD library has plenty more functions available but these examples are just to show you how simple it can be to add this display to your Pi project.

A more modern and stylish version of the small LCD display can be found in the Display-O-Tron units from the DOG Series of displays by the manufacturer, Electronic Assembly, **Figure 12-7**. Most suppliers stock the 3-line version that provides 3 lines of text, each with 16 characters. The display is very compact, low power and can run directly from a 3.3V supply, thus eliminating the over-voltage risk of combining 3.3V and 5V systems. If buying the bare display, you will find that the clip-on backlight is supplied separately, so you can choose from a range of colours. There is also a trans-reflective version of the display that can be used without a backlight when there's sufficient ambient lighting. The integrated controller for the display is an ST7036 device that can emulate the common HDD44780 protocol, but also offers an SPI serial interface. The only additional circuitry required to support 3.3V operation, is a couple of 1µF capacitors for the charge-pump.

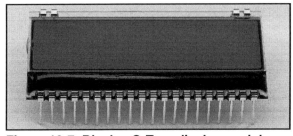

Figure 12-7: Display-O-Tron display module.

Figure 12-8: Display-O-Tron HAT on a Pi4B.

Many suppliers now have the Display-O-Tron unit integrated into a Pi HAT to create everything you need to control many automation projects. In addition to the display, the HAT features an RGB backlight so you can have any colour mix you like! There are also 6 capacitive-touch buttons, a 6-LED bar graph and several GPIO pins are exposed for connecting to peripherals, **Figure 12-8**.

You should refer to the supplier's website for access to up-to-date Python libraries, but I'll give you a few examples here to show how simple it is to use the Display-O-Tron.

To use the library in a Python program, you need to import it as follows:

```
from dothat import lcd
```

To write a message to the LCD at the current cursor position, you just need:

```
lcd.write("Hello")
```

To clear the display it's:

```
lcd.clear()
```

You can also adjust the contrast from the program instead of having to twiddle a pot. Here's how:

```
lcd.set_contrast(50)
```

The contrast number can be any integer value between 0 and 64.

In practice, we usually want a message to appear on a specific part of the display, so we need to tell the display where to start. We do that with the cursor position command, like so:

```
lcd.set_cursor_position(5 , 0)
```

In this command, the first digit is the column in the range 0 to 15 and the second digit is the row in the range 0 to 2. So, this example puts the cursor in the 6th column of the 1st row (NB: both start from 0).

To further illustrate these commands, here's simple Python program that displays Hello consecutively on each line of the display. The hash # and text that follows are my comments to explain the purpose of each line of code.

```
from dothat import lcd # Import the lcd code from the
dothat library

from time import sleep # Import the sleep function so we
can add delays

lcd.clear() #Clear the display before we begin

For r in range (0, 3): # Start a program loop that will
end when r reaches 3

    lcd.set_cursor_position(0, r) # Move the cursor to the
    start of line r

    lcd.write("Hello") # Write the message to the screen

    sleep(2) # Wait for 2 seconds

lcd.clear() # Clear the display ready for the next mes-
```

```
sage

# At this point, r will be incremented by 1 and the pro-
gram will loop back to the For statement

lcd.clear() # Clear the display

lcd.set_cursor_position(0, 0) # Move the cursor to the
first row/column

lcd.write("Program complete") # Display the final message
and finish
```

Medium resolution and touch-screen displays: One of the best medium resolution screens to use with the Pi is the official Pi 7" touch display. This is an excellent quality, well priced unit that is robust and uses a good quality IPS display along with full touch and gesture facilities. Another benefit comes from its use of the Display Serial Interface (DSI) thus leaving most the GPIO pins available. Many of the Pi screen competitors use the GPIO pins for the display, thus significantly reducing access for peripherals. The Official Pi display offers 800 x 480 pixels and uses an adapter board to interface between the DSI connector and the raw display, **Figure 12-9**. This adapter board is located behind the screen so Pi HATs and other expansion boards can be added to the top of the Pi. If you use the touch screen facilities, the adapter board needs access to the I2c pins on the GPIO to carry the touch screen data. From an amateur radio perspective, this display's 7" and 800 x 480 pixel resolution means that it's too small to handle desktop radio applications, unless they have

Figure 12-9: Rear of the Official 7" screen.

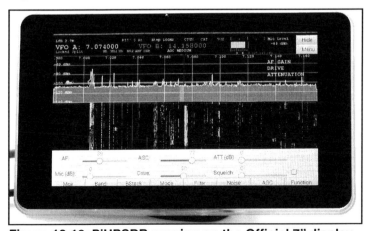

Figure 12-10: PiHPSDR running on the Official 7" display.

been specifically designed for use with low resolution screens. One of the particularly attractive applications for the 7" display is the PiHPSDR by John Molton, G0ORX, **Figure 12-10**. This free software creates a touch-screen interface for the popular ANAN and Hermes Lite transceivers that are offshoots from the HPSDR (High Performance Software Defined Radio) project. In addition to providing touch operation, PiHPSDR uses GPIO pins to support rotary encoders and manual switches to provide complete control of these high-performance transceivers.

Figure 12-11: Hyperpixel 4.0 display mounted of a Pi-4B.

In addition to the Official 7" screen, there are a huge range of 7" and smaller screens on the market. Most of these rely on using the GPIO pins for the video and control data, so access to the GPIO pins for other uses is often not possible. There's also plenty of competition in the 3" and 4" touch screen displays as these can be used for quite sophisticated user interfaces. A particularly attractive example being the HyperPixel 4.0, a 4" TFT display using a good quality IPS touch-panel panel and a resolution of 800 x 480 pixels, **Figure 12-11**. Once the drivers are installed, the 4" screen becomes the primary display for the Pi so it can be used with any software designed to operate with a 800 x 480 pixel screen. However, the small dimensions limit its usefulness for desktop applications.

Building graphic displays

Whilst it's relatively easy to build quite sophisticated applications on the Pi there will come a time when you need interaction between the Pi and its operator. For example, if you built a shack control system to control your rotator along with antenna switching and other common tasks would need two types of interface. The first is a hardware interface to send control signals to your rotator, control the antenna switch, etc. The second is an interface for the operator to use. In a traditional project this would comprise a project box with an array of knobs and switches etc. In my experience, constructing this physical interface and making it look good is often the most difficult part of any project. With the Pi we can build an all-electronic interface using one of the many touch screen displays. This type of interface is commonly called a Graphic User Interface or GUI. There are lots of ways to go about building such an interface, but many have a very steep learning curve, so are not best suited for use by occasional programmers. The most widely used of these is the Qt library, which is a very sophisticated package that comes complete with a visual programming application, so you can draw your own interface and then write the code to make it work. If you want to go down that route, there are many tutorials available on the web.

Simple GUI programming

For hobbyists and occasional programmers, there are several other GUI libraries that fit the bill. Two of the strongest contenders are GUIZero and my current favourite, PySimpleGUI. PySimpleGUI is a recent development (2018) and utilises several different mainstream GUI libraries to create a very easy-to-use system.

Introduction to GUI programming: Before we get to look at a code example, let me explain a basic principle of GUI programming. When writing many simple programs, we use sequential programming where we just step through a sequence of instructions taking actions where necessary. However, things change when using a GUI because the flow of the program is determined by the actions of the operator. In a typical GUI application, the software displays the GUI on the screen and then waits for the user tell it what to do. This is usually signalled by the user pressing a button, making a menu selection, etc. Behind the scenes the program is running in what's called an event loop where it repeatedly scans the touch screen or keyboard looking for a command from the operator. When it detects a command, it will activate the code associated with that part of the GUI.

The best way to get to grips with GUI programming is to try a simple example. Before you do that, you need to install the PySimpleGUI library on the Pi. This is very easy to do as follows:
1. Open a terminal session (Ctl-Alt-T)
2. Enter: sudo pip3 install pysimplegui
3. When complete, close the terminal session.

Example GUI program with PySimpleGUI:
Here is a simple GUI program that will draw a window on the screen with two buttons to either open the File Manager or Exit. You can try this for yourself by opening the Thonny IDE. Go to the Pi menu then select Programming - Thonny. Enter the following code making sure you use the same indenting. Once you've entered the code, save the file using a name of your choice with the py suffix, eg, myprog.py. You should be able to click the Run button in Thonny and the program window will appear. If it doesn't run, don't worry, as you've probably made a simple typing mistake. Look at the box at the bottom of Thonny and you will see some red text detailing the error. This usually includes a line number so you can start your search at that line.

```
import subprocess, PySimpleGUI as pygui

FM = r"/usr/bin/pcmanfm"
```

```
layout = [[ pygui.Button('File Manager'), pygui.
Button('Exit')]]

window = pygui.Window('Launch').Layout(layout)

while True:

   event, values = window.Read()

   if event is None or event == 'Exit':

   break

   if event == 'File Manager':

   sp = subprocess.Popen([FM,], shell=True,
stdout=subprocess.PIPE,          stderr=subprocess.PIPE)

window.Close()
```

How it Works:

The first line is used to import the Python libraries and you'll notice that I'm using an alias of 'pygui' for the PySimpleGUI library to save some typing. In the next line I've created a variable called FM to hold the path to the File Manager executable. If you want to use this Python script to run a different program, just change this line. The next line, beginning 'layout', is where I create the buttons. If you want more buttons you can add them here, separated by a comma. In the following line, I create the window for the application. I've left all the settings at the default so it will automatically adjust to fit the size of the buttons. Those four lines are all you need to create the GUI part of the program. The final few lines are a simple event loop using the 'While' statement. This will search for a button to be pressed and will either run the chosen program or exit depending on the selection.

When you've got this program running successfully, try adding extra buttons and running other programs.

PySimpleGUI is certainly a remarkably quick way to write GUIs and is ideal for experimenters. The documentation of the PySimpleGUI is excellent and I have found their Cookbook examples particularly useful. The Cookbook is packed with plenty of example programs that you can copy/paste in, to speed the development of your own programs.

Web displays

An alternative approach could be to use a web page to control your program. This frees the Pi from the need for a hardware display as you could access your Pi using another computer, smartphone or tablet. Web control can also be extended to provide remote access to your program via the Internet.

Building a smart and versatile web site is a complex task with a steep learning curve. However, if you're prepared to start with something a little more basic, there are some useful free tools that can smooth the path. The first is the Python Flask library. This is a microframework that provides some useful shortcuts for obtaining basic web server functionality. To give you an idea how simple it can be, the following code will create a basic webserver and return a page that says 'Hello Readers'.

```
from flask import Flask

app = Flask(__name__)

@app.route("/")

def hello():

    return "Hello Readers"
```

To see the results, do the following:
1. Open a terminal session and install flask with: sudo pip3 install flask
2. Enter the program lines into the Thonny IDE and save it as readers.py
3. Open a terminal session and run the server with:

```
FLASK_APP=readers.py flask run
```

4. Open a web browser on the Pi and navigate to: http://localhost:5000

You should see a plain web page with Hello Readers displayed at the top.

NB: When experimenting with flask, never name your Python script flask.py. If you do, it will fail, probably with an error message along the lines of cannot import Flask from flask. This will baffle you because the syntax in the program will be fine. Naming the script flask.py creates a naming conflict in flask that causes the error. If you do make this mistake, you will need to delete both the flask.py file and the generated flask.pyc file.

If you want to proceed on this route, there are plenty of Flask tutorials on the web and you should be able to find one that fits your learning style.

Summary

In this chapter we've examined a wide range of display options from a simple HDMI monitor through to basic software GUIs and web applications. Whilst self-contained projects with their own displays have their place, it's well worth investing time to learn how to create web-based applications. As we move into an era where everything can be controlled from your smartphone, tablet or PC, adding a web interface to our projects makes sense. In addition to the ease of access, a web-based interface gives you the flexibility to change the layout or add new features entirely in software.

Voice Control and AI

For many makers or electronics enthusiasts, the user interface is often the most difficult and time-consuming aspect of a project. It has become relatively easy to create web interfaces to our projects. Instead of using elaborate and expensive enclosures, complete with rotary controls, panel meters and buttons, we can leave our project as a black-box and operate the controls using a PC, tablet or even a smartphone. A software interface can also be combined with artificial intelligence (AI) to produce projects that can recognise our commands and speak to us. This may sound very science fiction, but the technology is available now and being driven by the likes of Amazon, Google and Microsoft.

DiY Artificial Intelligence

Google has recognised that the maker community can offer significant contributions to new technology and so have partnered with the Raspberry Pi team to make their AI platform available on the Pi. The project is known as Google Artificial Intelligence Yourself (AIY) and is based on the use of a Python SDK (Software Development Kit) that works with the Raspberry Pi. The idea became a reality in May 2017 when all subscribers to the print version of the Magpi magazine received a free Voice HAT, **Figure 13-1**. This was a complete kit and included microphone, speakers and a cardboard box to put it in. When combined with a Pi-3 and the supplied software, you could use the kit to create

Figure 13-1: Pi Voice HAT.

your own Google Assistant. Whilst the Google Assistant is surprisingly good and great for impressing your friends, the main benefit for us is access to Google's voice processing engine for controlling your own projects. As you will see in this chapter, it is very easy to program the Pi to switch GPIO pins or take other actions in response to voice commands. Whilst the Magpi project used the special Voice HAT expansion board, you can use any standard audio input/output device such as a USB sound card or a USB headset. The choice will depend on the project you have in mind.

Voice control

Let's begin with the voice element of the AIY project and I'll take a brief look at the vision options later. There are a couple of choices for installing the Google AIY software. The first is to use the dedicated Google AIY Pi image that's freely available for download. This is a complete working image based on the latest Raspbian OS but with all the additional software and configuration settings to work with the Voice HAT hardware. With that image installed, you need only create a Google account, add a new project and you're in business. The latest Google AIY image can be downloaded from: https://dl.google.com/dl/aiyprojects/aiyprojects-latest.img.xz

The second software option is to download the Google AIY project source and install it on an existing Pi system. This is a more complex process that's better suited for experienced programmers. The source code is available from the following link and installation instructions can be found in the file named HACKING.md. Here's the link: https://github.com/google/aiyprojects-raspbian

If you're using your own USB sound devices, the simplest and quickest way to get started is to use the preconfigured Raspbian AIY image that's designed for the Voice HAT but add a few configuration adjustments so that it uses your USB sound devices.

Using Google Voice services without the HAT

Because the Pi hardware has limited audio capabilities you will need to add a USB audio input/output device. The most obvious solution is to use a USB sound card and there are plenty on the market at around the £10 mark. I have used several and the UGREEN USB Audio Adapter (about £10) is a popular choice for the Pi because it has a short USB tail cable. This prevents the, often bulky soundcard, from blocking the closely spaced USB ports of the Pi. You can use many other USB sound devices such as a USB headset. I've been using a cheap MPOW USB headset for my tests. With the USB sound devices connected, we need to create an audio configuration file to tell Google Assistant to use our new device as the default sound device.

Begin by opening a terminal session and enter:

```
arecord -l
```

This will list the capture (recording) hardware that the Pi can see. You should see your card listed as a USB Audio Device. If you have a single USB sound card connected this will almost certainly show up as Card 1 device 0. Make a note of that and enter:

```
aplay -l
```

This will produce a similar list for the playback devices, so make a note of the card and device number for your new soundcard. With a single USB sound card connected, this will also show as Card 1, device 0. Next, we need to open a terminal session and create a new configuration file. Here is the process:

1. Open a terminal session and enter: cd ~
2. Create a configuration file by entering: sudo nano /etc/asound.conf
3. In the empty file that opens, add the following two lines:

```
defaults.pcm.card 1

defaults.ctl.card 1
```

4. Press Ctl-X followed by Y to save and close the file.

That completes the hardware configuration, so we can move on to the software.

Google Cloud - project setup

As you may have already guessed, Google speech is an online service that gives us access to Google's powerful voice analysis servers. To use the service, you need to create a free cloud account with Google. At the time of writing, Google was offering a 1-year free trial with $300 of usage credit. This generous offer has been made to encourage makers to experiment with their cloud services without having to worry about the cost. In addition, there is a free tier for all speech recognition products of 60 minutes usage per month. The net result is that the service will remain free unless we exceed the 60 minutes/month threshold. That 60 minutes is the time we're actually sending commands and receiving responses, so hobby projects should be ok.

Before you can setup a project and use the voice services, you need to have a free Google account. If you already have a Gmail account, you can use that. If not, just sign-up for a new Google account. Although there should be no charges for our very low usage rates, you will have to provide bank card details to get your cloud account. I'll show you the step-by-step instructions next but there is a risk the process may change in the future. In that event, the simple requirement here is to create a new Google Cloud project, add the Google Assistant and the Google Cloud Speech services and download the authorisation credentials. The process to achieve those simple tasks is a currently a bit convoluted. However, you only have to do this once for each project. Here are the project setup steps:

1. Begin by signing into the Cloud Console: https://console.cloud. google.com

2. Once signed-in, you can create a project by clicking the "select a project" drop-down that's next to the Google Cloud Platform title.

3. In the box that appears, click the New Project icon to create and name a new project. Ideally, you want a simple but descriptive name that's likely to be unique. For radio amateurs a simple way to make it unique it to include your callsign. For example, I used g4wnc-test as a project name.

4. When you've entered your project name, you will see the Project ID appear on the line below. If your project name is unique, the project ID will be the same as the project name but with dashes replacing any spaces, which is convenient for later parts of the process. You will also see that the Project ID can be edited by clicking on the Edit button.

5. With the name and Project ID set you can click the Create button to return to the cloud console.

6. Use the drop-down at the top of the page to select your new project, **Figure 13-2**.

7. Double click the name of your project and on the following screen click the menu icon (3 horizontal bars) and choose APIs and Services - Dashboard.

8. Click the Enable APIs and Services icon at the top of the page. In the search box enter Assistant and you should see the Google Assistant API in the panel below.

9. Select the Google Assistant and click Enable.

10. Go back one step to the "API Library home page" and search for Speech and choose the Cloud Speech to text API and enable it.

11. Now we need to create the authorisation credentials.

12. Use the menu to go back to the APIs and Services Dashboard and select Credentials then the OAuth consent screen.

13. Make sure the correct email address is showing and enter an application name, which can be the same as the project name. The remaining fields are optional.

14. Click the Save button at the bottom of the page.

15. In the Credentials panel, click the Create Credentials button and choose OAuth client ID.

16. You will be asked for your Application type and you should choose Other, amend the Name to Raspberry Pi and press Create to produce the Client ID and secret.

17. Click OK to close this panel and

Figure 13-2: Select project.

reveal the Credentials screen with your Raspberry Pi ID listed, Click OK.

18. At the end of the line with the Pi details, click on the download icon to download a .json file.
19. Rename the downloaded file to assistant.json and store it in the Pi home folder.
20. Next, we need to create credentials for the speech recognition API.
21. From the Credentials screen, click Create credentials – Service account key, New service account.
22. Give the service the same name as the project and change the role to Project Owner. Make sure JSON is selected as the key type and press Create to download the key. Click OK to complete.
23. Rename the downloaded json file to cloud_speech.json and store it in the Pi home folder.
24. We're nearly finished but need to sign-in to Google and activate the services.
25. Go to this page: myaccount.google.com/activitycontrols and make sure the blue slider switch is set to on for the following services: Web & App Activity, Location History, Device Information and Voice & Audio Activity (as Google changes the webpage content you may need to link to other pages to complete these settings). Close the Web browser when finished.

That completes the configuration and your Pi is now ready to use the Google Cloud speech services. If you are using the AIY Voice HAT you can use the supplied example programs to test it. You will find the examples in: home/pi/AIY-projects-python/src/examples/voice/. These examples also provide useful templates for creating your own applications. However, if you're using your own USB sound devices some of the examples will need to be modified. This specifically applies to those that require a button press or light an LED.

Using the Google Voice Services

You will have noticed from the previous section, that your new project is linked to both the Google Assistant and the Cloud Speech services. They both provide speech decoding facilities but have a different approach, as I'll explain here.

Google Assistant: This is a two-way speech service where you can ask questions or issue commands and Google Assistant will speak back to you. The Assistant can be triggered either by pressing a button, if you have the AIY HAT, or by using the hot phrase 'OK, Google'. This is the service that you will have seen advertised and gives you a two-way interaction with the Google Assistant. Whilst getting answers to random questions is fun, you can also use it to execute local tasks. You do this by adding your own 'hot Phrases' that, when detected, will execute your code. This can be accompanied by Google responding with a phrase of your choice. We'll look at that in more detail later.

Google Speech to Text:
This is easier to use but is limited to providing a speech to text conversion that's triggered by a button press. The result of the conversion is passed back into Python so it becomes easy to search the returned text and run code when a specific word or phrase is detected.

Examples

I recommend starting with the Google AIY SD card image as it will save you a lot of time. The image contains some excellent code examples that you can use as the starting point for your own applications. In the two examples that follow, you can create new voice activated applications with just a few lines of code.

Google Assistant: The best example program for Google Assistant based experiments is called:

```
assistant_library_with_local_commands_demo.py
```

This can be found in: /home/pi/AIY-projects-python/src/examples/voice

In this example program, we can add our own command phrases and define the action to take when that phrase is detected. Here's a short extract from the example file that shows the code used to detect the phrase 'power off' and shutdown the Pi. When writing Python code, we define functions with 'def' before they are called. Here is the function that will power off the Pi:

```
def power_off_pi():

    aiy.audio.say('Good bye!')

    subprocess.call('sudo shutdown now', shell=True)
```

This snippet begins with the name of the function (power_off_pi) and then tells the assistant to respond to the command by saying 'Good bye'. The final line runs the Shell command to shut down the Pi.

Let's now look at the corresponding code snippet that detects the 'Power off' phrase and calls the function.

```
text = event.args['text'].lower()

    if text == 'power off':

        assistant.stop_conversation()

            power_off_pi()
```

In this snippet, the first line collects the phrase that Google Assistant has just heard and stores it into a variable called 'text'. The second line checks 'text' to see if it contains the phrase we're looking for, eg 'power off'. If the phrase is detected, the Assistant is stopped (assistant.stop_conversation) and the function power_off_pi is called. If the phrase is not detected, the program just keeps listening. In the supplied example programs, you will see these two code segments are repeated for each of the key words or phrases. If you look at the example carefully, you will see that the subsequent code snippets begin with elif instead of if. This is a Python shortened command for 'else, if', which means if the previous test wasn't matched, then try another. This is the standard Python technique that's used to link a series of if tests.

I hope you can see from this simple example, that using the Google Assistant to detect phrases and run Python functions is remarkably easy.

Google Speech to Text:
This is simpler to use than the Assistant and the example program is much shorter. You'll find the example program in the same directory as before:

```
/home/pi/AIY-projects-python/src/examples/voice
```

The speech to text example we're using is called:

```
cloudspeech_demo.py
```

In this example, Google can't talk back but it listens continuously and converts any speech that it detects into text. This code snippet from cloudspeech_demo.py, receives the converted speech in the variable 'text' and searches for the key phrases using if and elif statements as in the previous example. However, this example doesn't use a separate function to carry out the tasks but directly alters the state of the LED. The decision as to whether to act directly or use a function depends on the complexity of the task you want to perform. My preference would be to use a function because it clearly separates the detection and action code and thus makes the code easier to maintain or customise.

```
text = text.lower()

    if 'turn on the light' in text:

        board.led.state = Led.ON

    elif 'turn off the light' in text:

        board.led.state = Led.OFF

    elif 'blink the light' in text:

        board.led.state = Led.BLINK

    elif 'goodbye' in text:

        break
```

Google Voice services manual install
The Google voice services are packaged in the Google Voice SDK (Software Development Kit). This is a Python based set of tools that we can use to access and build our own Google Voice applications. However, the SDK has several Python requirements that conflict with the preinstalled Python versions in the standard Raspbian distribution. It's for that reason that I recommend using the official Google image. However, if you do require a manual install, you can make

use of Python's virtual environment. This is a Python feature that lets us isolate conflicting Python systems from each other. This is essentially a new directory tree where we can install and run our voice software and the associated Python libraries without disturbing the Pi default Python installation. The Google official installation guidance can be seen here: https://developers.google.com/assistant/sdk/guides/library/python/

Next steps - vision and beyond

Voice technology is developing very quickly and there are many other players out there that have offerings available for developers. Most rely on a network connection but there are a few standalone voice processing systems. However, I've yet to find one that runs successfully on a Pi. I'm sure that situation will change soon as voice-controlled appliances become commonplace. Google have already launched an AIY Vision project (£125) that's capable of recognising a surprisingly large number of objects. This currently works with the Pi Zero and is reliant on a specialist video chip that does most of the hard work. Most of the machine learning and AI work is currently achieved using TensorFlow, an open source software library for high performance numerical computation. This work is being supported with the development of new hardware TensorFlow Processing Units (TPUs). These are new to the market and the first to be available for the Pi was the Google Edge TPU, **Figure 13-3** This is a small USB connected device for the Pi that includes a specialised Google ASIC device that carries out the AI heavy lifting. The use of the term 'Edge' refers to devices that are at the edge of IoT networks. These are often relatively simple devices such as temperature sensors and the like but increasingly, they have a need to be able to learn or respond to voice or image inputs. The Google Edge TPU works particularly well with the new Pi-4B as it can use the full speed USB 3 ports to speed the data flows.

Figure 13-3: Google Edge TPU.

Summary

It is quite remarkable how quickly speech and vision related interfaces are developing. All the major players in the electronics and computing world are ploughing huge investments into this field. As hobbyists, we can reap the benefits through the services that are made available to the open source community. Releasing products to open source users is a great way for the big players to field-test and refine their software, so everybody wins.

Other Single Board Computers

The Raspberry Pi's unrivalled success is testament to the excellent choices made by the Raspberry Pi team in the overall design of the Pi. Not surprisingly, many others have attempted to benefit from the Pi's popularity by producing a range of look-alike boards. At the heart of the Pi and its competitors is the use of a System on a Chip (SoC) device. This can take many forms but, in the case of Single Board Computers (SBC), the SoC is a single integrated circuit package that typically contains several processor cores, a Graphics Processing Unit (GPU) and other supporting elements, **Figure 14-1**. Combining these functions in a single chip reduces the physical space requirements and helps simplify the printed circuit board (PCB) layout. This is because the complex 32 or 64-line bus interconnections between processors, GPU, etc. are made inside the SoC. The driver for the development of these fast and highly integrated devices has been the smartphone market. Smartphones sell globally in huge quantities and many users expect to upgrade their devices every year or two. This huge demand funds the high development costs and we get to enjoy the spoils through access to a source of constantly improving SoCs. The Pi has enjoyed very close relations with Broadcom since its inception and all the Pi models use a Broadcom SoC at their core. The other SBCs that I've covered here use either the Rockchip or Allwinner SoC devices.

Figure 14-1: Pi System on a Chip SoC.

These Pi competitors usually have a few performance tweaks so they can be advertised as offering an advantage over the original Pi. You should be very cautious when reading these comparisons as they are usually skewed to make the most of the SBC they're promoting. You also need to check the Pi model used for the comparison. I've seen examples where the comparison is made against a Model B Pi. However, this often turns out to be the original Model B with its single-core processor running at 900MHz. That's a long way from the current Pi-3 Model B+ with its 64-bit quad-core processor running at 1.4GHz!

The most common enhancements are to add full Gigabit Ethernet and USB 2 ports. This addresses a known bottleneck in the Pi and is relatively easy to achieve with readily available single-chip solutions. However, these enhancements increase both the cost and power consumption of the board. Whist Gigabit Ethernet or USB 2 ports can be useful for some applications, this needs to be matched with a faster processor to handle the increased data load. In addition to a few performance and connectivity enhancements, many of the other SBCs support running the Android operating system, if that is important for your application.

One of the Pi features that has worked particularly well is the standardised, General Purpose Input Output (GPIO) connector. Even though this was increased from 26-pins to 40-pins early in the Pi's development, the first 26 pins retained their original functionality. This consistency is important as it gives 3rd party manufacturers the confidence to develop their accessories in the knowledge that they will continue to be useful across a wide range of Pi models. The result is a very vibrant and competitive market for Pi accessories. Many of the competing SBCs retain the Pi GPIO layout and functionality so they too can benefit from the established accessory market.

SBC Operating Systems

When considering moving to a different SBC you need to check the availability of Operating Systems (OSes) because standard Raspbian will only run on Raspberry Pi hardware. Without a stable and well-developed OS, the speed and power of the new SBC may well be unusable. The best way to check-out SBC OSes is to read online reviews and check the forums for other people's experiences.

ASUS Tinker Board:
This was launched back in 2017 by this major PC hardware manufacturer, **Figure 14-2**. The Tinker Board is well built and matches the physical features of the Pi very closely. So close, in fact, that it fits the Official Pi cases, **Figure 14-3**. Processing power comes from a Rockchip ARM Quad-core CPU that operates at speeds up to 1.8GHz. This is supported with 2GB of LPDDR3 memory. As in the Pi, the Tinker Board has a dedicated Graphics Processing Unit (GPU) and can handle UHD video at 30FPS. Another welcome addition to the Tinker Board is the integrated 192ksps/24-bit audio CODEC so there is no need to use an external soundcard. The four USB 2.0 ports have a dedicated controller that is independent of the Ethernet controller, thus negating that potential bottleneck. The network port also supports full Gigabit speeds.

Full Wi-Fi and Bluetooth LE is provided but it doesn't have support for the higher-speed 5GHz Wi-Fi as provided in the Pi-3B+ and A+ boards. As the Tinker Board uses a Rockchip processor, it won't run Pi Raspbian. However, ASUS do provide a custom Linux image for free download. This image was rather fragile when first launched and received lots of criticism, but it has improved over time. An excellent alternative is the ARMbian variant of Linux that's available for many of SBC models including the Tinker Board. I've used ARMbian with the Tinker Board and found it to be very stable. When launched, the Tinker Board was very competitively priced, but the price difference has gradually increased. At the time of writing, the standard Tinker Board was available for £59.99 whereas the Pi-3B+ was £32.81, from the same

Figure 14-2: ASUS Tinker Board.

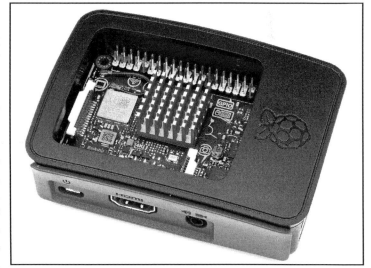

Figure 14-3: Tinker Board in a Pi case.

supplier. ASUS have recently launched an updated version in the Tinker Board S. The main processing power remains unchanged, but it includes a few operating refinements and an onboard 16GB eMMC storage device for faster booting and file access. The new model also carries a significant price increase to £99.

ODROID:

These SBC's are produced by the South Korean company Hardkernel and include a range of powerful designs. The only models that retain significant Pi compatibility are the C1+ and the C2. The C1+ uses a quad-core, 32-bit ARM CPU running at 1.5GHz and supported by 1GB of DDR3 SDRAM. The onboard video processor is a 2-core ARM Mali unit that is capable of handling 4k 60FPS video, which may be important for some, especially if using the ODROID as the heart of a media-centre. Pricing for the C1+ is also very competitive at £40.90. The more powerful C2, features an all-round performance boost with a 64-bit ARM quad-core CPU running at 1.5GHz with 2GB of DDR3 SDRAM. The Mali GPU capacity is also increased to include 3-pixel and 2-shader cores and supports 4k 60fps video. The more powerful C2 comes at a premium and the current cost is £71.20.

Banana Pi Range:
There are a wide range of boards available from this Chinese manufacturer but here I'll look at three that are closest to the Pi format. The Banana Pi M2 Berry follows the Pi model B format closely, but the significant addition is a SATA port. This makes it particularly suitable for use as a media server or in other applications where fast hard disk access is desirable. The M2 Berry also includes Gigabit Ethernet, Bluetooth and Wi-Fi but not the faster 5GHz Wi-Fi, as available in the Pi-3B+. The M2 processor SoC is an Allwinner A7 V40 unit. If you need more power, the Banana Pi M3 steps up to an Octa-core processor running at 1.8GHz and includes a SATA port for fast disk access. Price for the Banana Pi M3 is around £76 but I found it difficult to find stocks. The final model I mention here is the Banana Pi Zero that uses the Pi Zero format but includes a quad-core A7 processor along with Bluetooth and Wi-Fi, making it a particularly powerful miniature SBC. However, it was impossible to find a dealer with stocks at the time of writing, but I've included it here for completeness.

Nano Pi:
This series of SBCs is from Chinese manufacturer FriendlyElec. However, none of the models use the Pi physical format, though a few include a Pi compatible GPIO connector. The A64 features a quad-core 1.152GHz CPU and a Mali GPU supported by 1GB DDR3 RAM. In addition to standard USB 2.0, the A64 includes a full Gigabit Ethernet port and a Pi compatible 40-pin GPIO connector. The A64 is available direct from China for approximately £20 plus carriage and import taxes. The NanoPi M1 is a low power option that has a quad-core 1.2GHz processor, 10/100 Ethernet, 3 x USB2.0 ports and onboard audio. The NanoPi M1 is available direct from China at £15 plus carriage and import taxes.

Orange Pi:
There are a large range of board variants available from this Chinese manufacturer, but I'll just look at a couple here. The Orange Pi 3 uses a quad-core 64-bit, 1.8GHz ARM Cortex A53 based SoC that includes a Mali-T720 GPU. The processor is supported with 1GB DDR3 RAM and the Ethernet is standard 10/100Mbs. USB connectivity includes 4 x USB 2.0 ports plus a USB On The Go (OTG) port. This allows the Orange Pi 3 to look like a USB device when plugged into the USB port of another computer and loaded with the appropriate software. The Orange Pi 3 also features an audio CODEC and accepts video

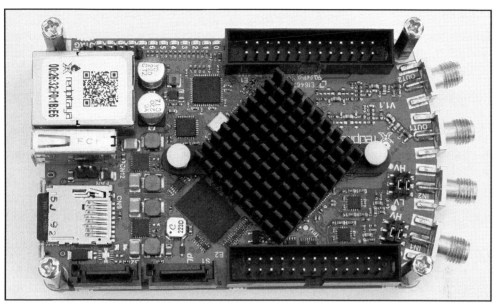

Figure 14-4: Red Pitaya.

input at a maximum rate of 1080p and 30fps. At the time of writing the Orange Pi 3 was only available direct from China where the price was $39.90US. The second device I'll cover here is the Orange Pi PC Plus that is another Pi look-alike based on an Allwinner H3 quad-core Cortex A7 processor with HDMI 4k video support and 1GB DDR3 RAM that's shared with the GPU. The Orange Pi PC Plus also features 8GB of eMMC flash that can be used to store the operating system. This enables faster boot times along with rapid file access. The Orange Pi PC is again only available direct from China at $41.90US.

Red Pitaya:
This is a bit of an odd-ball to include here because it has no obvious relationship with a Pi but is a form of SBC and has many features that make it attractive for amateur radio use, **Figure 14-4**. I have in the past included material on the Red Pitaya in my radio PowerPoint presentations. The Red Pitaya comprises three significant main components:

Dual Analogue to Digital Converters (ADC):
These can read analogue DC through to HF signals and digitise them ready for processing in an SDR receiver. They can also be used to digitise signals for processing with digital oscilloscope or spectrum analyser software. In effect, with the addition of the right software, the Red Pitaya can become a powerful multifunction bench instrument.

Dual Digital to Analogue Converters (DAC):
The opposite of an ADC, these devices convert a digital input into its equivalent analogue output. That enables operation as a signal generator or an HF transmitter.

Field Programmable Gate Array (FPGA):
This is a programmable logic device that can be configured to perform a wide range of functions. One of its major attractions is the ability to parallel process high speed data, thus making it ideal for SDR receivers and test instrument emulation.

The original Red Pitaya featured dual 14-bit ADCs with a maximum sample rate of 125MSPS, when combined with its original price point of around £230 this made it an attractive proposition for the heart of an Amateur Radio direct sampling SDR transceiver for the HF through to 50MHz bands.
Whilst the Red Pitaya has tremendous potential, realising that potential requires one of two options to be available:

    1 - You need to have the time and capability to master FPGA and SDR programming techniques. This is not a trivial task and FPGA programming in particular is very specialised.

OR

    2 - You need to locate a source of pre-written software/firmware for the Red Pitaya that will meet your requirements.

The Red Pitaya does have some free, pre-written, test equipment, software available but these have limited capabilities, and, in my experience, many applications have poor user interfaces and are prone to crashing.
From an amateur radio perspective, there is a single engineer that has done some excellent work with the Red Pitaya. Pavel Demin is a young software engineer who has developed code for the Red Pitaya to emulate an HPSDR (High Performance SDR) Hermes transceiver. That means it can be accessed via the Ethernet and operated by any software that's designed for use with the popular Hermes boards. The emulation works very well, and Pavel has also developed a multi-band WSPR transceiver, and an excellent HF Vector Network Analyser (VNA), using the Red Pitaya. However, to make a practical amateur radio transmitter, you still need to provide a PA stage, adequate, switchable filtering and transmit/receive switching.
In addition to the original 14-bit model, Red Pitaya have launched a cheaper 12-bit model. This has the same sample rates as it's bigger sibling but is restricted to 12-bit samples. The latest model to be announced features 16-bit sampling and a modified sample rate of 122.8MHz, which matches that of the Hermes SDR boards. As you might expect, this is going to be much more expensive and the recommended price is in the region of £510 plus shipping, so probably

close to £550. You would also need to add a PA stage, filtering and transmit/ receive switching to form a complete transceiver.

When looking at SDR options with boards such the Red Pitaya, there's a temptation to compare them with popular amateur transceivers and see them as offering a cheap solution. However, a few words of caution are appropriate. The Red Pitaya was designed to be used as a development board in an educational environment. As a result, it is not intended for continuous operation nor for operating in harsh environments. If the board fails you are on your own, as the Red Pitaya team don't offer a repair service. Also, because the board could have been connected to many different devices, it is virtually impossible to prove that a failure was due to a manufacturing fault, as opposed to some external factor. From personal experience, I had a power regulator failure after about two years and Red Pitaya offered no support at all. If you compare a home-built transceiver based on the new 16-bit Red Pitaya with the popular Elad FDM-DUO, it's very hard to make a case for the Red Pitaya. Once you've added the PA, filters, antenna switching, power supplies and enclosures, the cost will be close to £600 or £700, whereas the Elad can be bought with full dealer back up and repair service for about £900!

By far the best role for a board such as the Red Pitaya is as an educational tool to help you develop your own programming skills.

Troubleshooting

Introduction

When you start using the Pi you will inevitably encounter a few problems. Many of these may be due to a lack of familiarity with Linux, whilst others will be due to oddities of the Pi hardware. One important point to remember is that Linux generally does exactly what you ask it to do, often without any further prompts or warnings. This makes the system very responsive, but, if you inadvertently ask it to do something silly, such as deleting the operating system, it will just get on and do it! The most common problem with command line work is errors in capitalisation or spacing. Everything in Linux is case sensitive. If a command is not doing what you expect, check the use of capitals and spaces. A common scenario in Linux is to enter a command followed by an argument, ie ls /dev/tty*. In this command, there must be a space between ls and /dev or it will throw an error. I also find it very helpful to walk away from a problem and do something else for a while. With the pressure removed, I often find the grey cells clunk away and I have a eureka moment that solves the problem!

Erratic behaviour or random failures

Power supply problems are the most common cause of seemingly random failures. Whilst the use of USB sockets for power input is very convenient, USB cables can cause problems. If you stick to an 'Official' Pi power supply you should be fine, as they use heavy gauge wire and provide a 5.1V or 5.2V feed to overcome any small voltage drops in the cable or USB connector. However, many consumer grade USB cables use very fine conductors to make the cables more flexible and easier to use. It is these cables that often have an excess voltage drop and can result in an unstable power feed to the Pi. To help identify these problems, the Pi has an integrated voltage detector that will display a lightning bolt icon on the screen if it detects a low voltage. However, this detector often fails to spot small glitches, so can't be relied upon for power problem detection. If you need to purchase a better quality USB cable, choose one that is recommended for fast-charging mobile phones. These must be able to supply up to 2.4A so are likely to use thicker wires with a correspondingly lower voltage drop.

SD Cards can also be a source of random problems and Linux has built-in tools to help. The Linux command fsck (File System ChecK) provides a well-established file system error detection and repair service. You rarely need to use this manually because the system will automatically trigger fsck if it detects a disk error. However, fsck can only run on unmounted disks so it doesn't run immediately. Instead, the operating system will mark the disk as requiring repair and fsck will run automatically during the next boot process. If you think you have a corrupt SD card, try re-booting the Pi a couple of times and fsck will do its best to repair it. If you want to force fsck to run, add the following to the end of the command line in /boot/cmdline.txt:

```
fsck.mode=force
```

Whilst microSD cards are a very convenient solution for the Pi operating system, they have a limited lifespan so it's well worth keeping a backup and periodically replacing heavily used cards.

Specific problems

Like all computer systems, there are a few common problems that are experienced by Pi users, so I'll cover those here:

Missing menu bar:
This can happen if lxpanel crashes or the lxpanel configuration file is damaged. The solution is simple, so follow these steps:
1. Press Ctl-Alt-T to open a terminal session
2. Enter the following to delete to current config details:

```
sudo rm -r ~/.config/lxpanel
```

3. Enter: sudo startx
4. Press: Ctl-Alt-F6 to get a terminal session and log-in.
5. Enter: startx to begin a new LXpanel session
6. That's it.

Virtual Memory Exhausted:
When compiling software from source, you may experience a crash or failure due to a shortage of virtual memory. This is often reported with the error: Virtual memory exhausted: Cannot allocate memory. This is most likely to occur when compiling software from source on an early model Pi or Pi Zero with

a small on-board RAM. When this RAM is exhausted, Linux will start using what's known as a swap file. The swap file is reserved space on the SD card that's set aside to be used as virtual memory. Increasing the swap file size is a simple process and will fix the problem. Here's a step-by-step guide:

1. Open a terminal session (Ctl-Alt-T)
2. Enter: sudo nano /etc/dphys-swapfile
3. Scroll to the line: CONF_SWAPSIZE=100
4. Change this to read: CONF_SWAPSIZE=1024
5. Press Ctl-X followed by Y and Enter to save and close the file.

If you still run out of virtual memory, replace 1024 in step 4 with 2048. An alternative technique is to automatically set the swap file to twice the size of the on-board RAM. Here's how:

1. Open a terminal session (Ctl-Alt-T)
2. Enter: sudo nano /etc/dphys-swapfile
3. Scroll to the line: #CONF_SWAPFACTOR=2
4. Change this to remove the "#" at the beginning of the line
5. Press Ctl-X followed by Y and Enter to save and close the file.

When you've finished compiling the program, it's important to restore the swap file back to its original size to avoid excessive use of the SD card.

Fixing a slow mouse:

Back in 2014 the OS was altered to enforce a fixed mouse polling rate of 62.5Hz. This was to stop some high-performance mice from demanding unreasonably high update rates. However, this change does not suit all mice, and some may become very slow. The fix is to add a command to the cmdline.txt file that runs at start-up. Here's the step-by-step process to make the change:

1. Open a terminal session (Ctl-Alt-T)
2. Enter: sudo nano /boot/cmdline.txt
3. This will open the file in the nano text editor. This file contains a single line of commands. NB: This must be kept as a single line.
4. Use the arrow keys to move the cursor to the end of the line, add a space then enter:

   ```
   usbhid.mousepoll=0
   ```

5. Close and save the file by pressing Ctl-X followed by Y then Enter
6. Now restart the Pi by entering: reboot

NB: All commands in this file must be on the same single line. If you need to revert, repeat the above steps but delete usbhid.mousepoll=0 from the end of the command line.

External hard drive or USB device not visible:

This occurs most frequently on earlier Pi models that have limited USB power-feed capabilities. In these cases, the external device attempts to draw more current than the Pi can provide and therefore it fails. The simplest solution is to use a powered USB hub to connect the target drive.

No screen display:

A common cause of no display is to connect the HDMI monitor after the Pi has finished booting. It's important to connect the HDMI screen before power-up because the Pi checks for a valid display during the boot process. If it doesn't detect a valid HDMI device, it automatically sends composite video to the 3.5mm video/audio jack. If necessary, you can force the Pi to provide an HDMI output by adding or uncommenting the following lines in /boot/config.txt:

```
hdmi_forcehotplug=1
```

```
hdmi_drive=2
```

Blank HDMI screen after using Pi 7" touch screen: If you've been using a touch screen and want to revert to a standard HDMI monitor, you may find that the Pi refuses to switch back. In that case, add the following line to /boot/config.txt:

```
ignore_lcd+1
```

NB: You will need to delete this entry if you want to use the touch screen again.

Password reset:

The Pi Linux distributions are supplied with a default user/password combination of pi/raspberry. If you change the password, you must keep a note of the new password as it is not recoverable. In the event of a lost password, the only option is to reset and choose a new password.

Scenario 1: If your Pi automatically boots to the desktop without requiring a password. Here's how to do the password reset:

1. From the Pi menu choose Preferences - Raspberry Pi Configuration - Change Password
2. Enter your new password twice.

Scenario 2: A Pi that only boots to the command line Interface and requires login:

1. Remove the SD card and connect it to another computer using a card reader.
2. Access the SD card using File Explorer or similar and open the file: cmdline.txt in a simple text editor.
3. Move your cursor to the end of the long single line and add a space.
4. Add the following text to the end of that line:
   ```
   init=bin/sh
   ```
5. NB: Do not add a Return at the end of the line.
6. Save the file and eject the SD card from your computer.

7. Replace the card in your Pi and power it up.
8. You will be presented with a screen full of text and a flashing cursor at the bottom.
9. Enter:

```
su
```

10. This will log you in as the root user.
11. Enter:

```
passwd pi
```

12. Follow the prompts and enter your new password twice.
13. You should see a line of text confirming that the password has been successfully updated.
14. If the update fails and you see a 'token manipulation error', enter the following:

```
sudo mount -o remount,rw /dev/mmcblk0p2 /
```

15. Retry from step 9 above.

Once you've successfully updated the password, power-down the Pi, remove the SD card and delete the text you added to the cmdline.txt file in step 4. Your Pi should now boot normally.

Finding help online

If you're stuck with a Pi problem, the Internet is your friend and the Raspberry Pi official forums are a good place to start. These can be found at: https://www.raspberrypi.org/forums/ and are divided into subject groups. For the new user, the forum search panel near the top of the page provides a simple way to search the entire site. However, you need to take care to be specific with your problem description to limit the number of results displayed.

If the Pi forums don't provide the answer, then a wider Internet search is the way to go. However, if you don't plan your internet search carefully, the results can be overwhelming. For those that are new to solving problems via the Internet, I've provided the following tips to set you off in the right direction.

When starting a search, I usually begin by entering Raspberry Pi followed by a description of the problem I'm trying to solve. For example, to look for solutions to a slow mouse I would enter: 'Raspberry Pi slow mouse'

By putting Raspberry Pi at the start of the query it helps filter the search results to be Pi related. If you are inundated with responses the next step can be to filter the results by time. This is available in the Google search engine by choosing 'Tools – Any time' and then selecting the age of results you want to consider. By using the time filter, you can be more confident of finding an up to date solution. However, if you get very few relevant responses you may need to open-up your search criteria.

Of course, there are times where your query might be related to a programming language or even the Linux operating system. In that case make sure you add the language or Linux to the beginning of the query. For example, if I wanted to find some Python 3 code samples to help me convert a voltage measurement into dBm, I would use the following: 'Python 3 convert voltage to dBm' This a more unusual query that may not produce a simple answer, so you may need to open-up the query by dropping Python 3. That will give a much wider range of responses and should still give you useful information that you can use to help solve the problem.

Alphabetic Index

Subject Index